It's Your Wellbeing

Senior Cycle SPHE

Fiona Chambers   Anne Jones   Anita Stackpoole

MENTOR

Mentor Books Ltd.,
43 Furze Road
Sandyford Industrial Estate
Dublin 18
Republic of Ireland

Tel: +353 1 295 2112/3
Fax: +353 1 295 2114
e-mail: admin@mentorbooks.ie
www.mentorbooks.ie

A catalogue record for this book is available from the British Library

The paper used in this book is made from the wood pulp of managed forests. For every tree felled, at least one tree is planted, thereby renewing natural resources.

ISBN: 978-1-912514-25-0

Cover Design: Kathryn O'Sullivan
Typesetting and layout: Mary Byrne
Editor: Emma Dunne

Acknowledgements
The publisher would like to thank the following for permission to reproduce copyright material: National Suicide Research Foundation; Department of Health; Road Safety Authority; AskAboutAlcohol.ie (Health Services Executive); Dublin North East Drugs task Force (text on types of drugs); Irish Family Planning Association; BeLonG To Youth Services; Getty Images; Thinkstock.

The publisher has made every effort to trace and acknowledge the holders of copyright for material in this book. In the event of any copyright holder being overlooked, the publishers will come to a suitable arrangement at the first opportunity.

Foreword

It's Your Wellbeing is based on the Senior Cycle SPHE programme, which helps you to understand your strengths so that you plan a life after school which celebrates your talents and abilities. Throughout the book, you will see Wellbeing Indicators (explained below) at key points, showing how a particular activity or concept can develop your wellbeing in this area. Numeracy and literacy indicators will show where these skills can be used. At this time, you may have a very clear idea of what you want to do after school. Equally, the thought of life after school might be a very confusing and daunting prospect. Either way, we have carefully picked out activities which allow you to explore and state your opinions in relation to important issues which will impact on your life now and in the future. We hope that these opportunities will fire your imagination and help you to find a pathway which is truly for you, a pathway which enables you to shine — body, mind and soul. We hope you enjoy this time of discovery, and we wish you happiness, health and success.

Fiona, Anne and Anita

 Numeracy skills   **Literacy skills**

INDICATORS OF WELLBEING

ACTIVE
- Am I a confident and skilled participant in physical activity?
- How physically active am I?

RESPONSIBLE
- Do I take action to protect and promote my wellbeing and that of others?
- Do I make healthy eating choices?
- Do I know where my safety is at risk and do I make right choices?

CONNECTED
- Do I feel connected to my school, my friends, my community and the wider world?
- Do I appreciate that my actions and interactions impact on my own wellbeing and that of others, in local and global contexts?

RESILIENT
- Do I believe that I have the coping skills to deal with life's challenges?
- Do I know where I can go for help?
- Do I believe that with effort I can achieve?

RESPECTED
- Do I feel that I am listened to and valued?
- Do I have positive relationships with my friends, my peers and my teachers?
- Do I show care and respect for others?

AWARE
- Am I aware of my thoughts, feelings and behaviours and can I make sense of them?
- Am I aware of what my personal values are and do I think through my decisions?
- Do I understand what helps me to learn and how I can improve?

CONT

Module 1:
Self-Management (Part 1)

Module 2:
Mental Health

Module 3:
Gender Studies

Module 4:
Substance Use

ENTS

For Matthew, Georgie, Donnacha, Sadhbh, Fiachra and Lena

'In any given moment we have two options: to step forward into
growth or step back into safety'

Abraham Maslow

'Education is not the preparation for life ... Education is life itself'

John Dewey

'There are only two days in the year that nothing can be done.
One is called yesterday and the other is called tomorrow, so today is the right day
to love, believe, do and mostly live.'

Dalai Lama

Module 1:
Self-Management (Part 1)

1. Life Plan

This section is about goal setting and getting the most out of your life, all while nurturing your mind, body and spirit. There are a couple of stages in this process:

- **Stage One: Personality Type** — Understanding yourself in terms of strengths and weaknesses.
- **Stage Two: Reality Check** — Identifying where you are now in your life.

Stage One: Personality Type

TICK BOX ACTIVITY

1. What kind of goal-setter are you?
   Tick ✓ the statement that applies to you.

   (a) I am an underachiever. I set goals all the time but I haven't achieved any of them yet. ☐

   (b) I am achieving but would like to achieve more. ☐

   (c) I do set goals but would like to learn a new way of doing it. ☐

WRITTEN ACTIVITY

2. Think about your life now and why you might need to set goals.
   Complete this sentence: *I need to set goals because*

   _____
   _____
   _____
   _____
   _____

Now let's look at you in more detail. What kind of personality do you have? This may determine your attitude to goal-setting. Choose the bird description below that best matches your personality.

Dove: The compassionate and peaceful dove. The dove is people orientated, loyal, friendly, hard working and a great team player but tends to avoid change, confrontation, risk taking and assertiveness.

Owl: The wise owl. The owl is logical, mathematically minded, methodical and sometimes seen as a perfectionist. The owl can be slow to make decisions and inflexible if rules and logic say otherwise. Owls are not big risk takers but love detail.

Peacock: The showy peacock. The peacock loves talking and being the centre of attention, has passion/enthusiasm and is happy/optimistic. Peacocks can be accused of talking too much and aren't good with detail or time-control.

Eagle: The bold eagle. Eagles are dominant, stimulated by challenge, decisive and direct. Eagles can be blunt/stubborn, lose sight of the big picture and insensitive to other people's needs. Eagles are natural achievers.

Source: www.achieve-goal-setting-success.com/behaviour-profile.html

WRITTEN ACTIVITY

3. Bird Types

(a) Which bird best describes you?

_____

_____

(b) How might this impact on your goal-setting?

_____

_____

_____

_____

_____

(c) Therefore, to get the best out of goal-setting, you should

_____

_____

_____

_____

_____

More fact-finding

(a) Try the Myers-Briggs Personality test. Read the first two lists left to right and decide if you are an Extrovert or an Introvert. Circle E or I. Do the same for the other three sets of lists. At the end of the process you will end up with four letters, e.g. ENTJ. This is your Myers-Briggs Personality type.

Myers-Briggs Short Test

EXTROVERT   E
- Sociable
- Outgoing
- Animated
- Expressive
- Acts before thinking
- Broad experience

PRACTICAL   S
- Down-to-earth
- Eye for detail
- Materialistic
- Trusts experience
- Values security
- Works systematically

COOL   T
- Seeks respect
- Critical
- Thinking
- Questions
- Independent
- Values truth

ORGANISED   J
- Planned approach
- Makes decisions
- Disciplined
- Sets goals
- Good at completing
- Controlled

INTROVERT   I
- Private
- Reserved
- Quiet
- Reflective
- Thinks before acting
- Deep experience

IMAGINATIVE   N
- Full of ideas
- Sees meaning
- Idealistic
- Trusts hunches
- Values freedom
- Works in bursts

WARM   F
- Seeks appreciation
- Supportive
- Feeling
- Trusts
- Belonging
- Values harmony

EASYGOING   P
- Flexible approach
- Keeps options open
- Haphazard
- Spots opportunities
- Good at exploring
- Spontaneous

Your personality type is determined by the preferred mode for each of the four pairs listed on the previous page. There are **16** possible combinations:

Thinking Types: ESTJ, ENTJ, ISTP, INTP
Intuitive Types: ENTP, ENFP, INFJ, INTJ
Feeling Types: ESFJ, ENFJ, ISFP, INFP
Sensory Types: ESTP, ESFP, ISFJ, ISTJ

WRITTEN ACTIVITY

4. Your Myers-Briggs personality type

(a)   What is your personality type? [i.e. four letters]

_____

_____

(b)   Which is your preferred type?

_____

_____

(c)   Is this a surprise to you? If so, why?

_____

_____

RESEARCH

5. See if you can find a famous person who shares your personality type.
   Search online for: Myers-Briggs famous type

(b) Now try the Gardner's (1983) Multiple Intelligences Test.
Work through each list of statements in turn.
Within each list:
– Tick ✓ each of the comments that describes you
– Then total the number of ticks in each list
That reveals your score for that particular intelligence.

Body Smart (Kinaesthetic Intelligence)

1. I do at least one sport in my free time.
2. I find it hard to sit still for a long time.
3. I like working with my hands to make things.
4. My best ideas come to me when I am walking or doing something.
5. I like to dance.
6. I need to touch things to learn about them.
7. I enjoy scary amusement rides.
8. I am not clumsy.
9. I like to learn by doing rather than reading how to do it.
10. I like to act things out to help me to remember.

Score out of ten: _____

Word Smart (Linguistic Intelligence)

1. Books are very important to me.
2. I can hear words in my head before I read, speak or write them down.
3. I prefer listening to the radio or audiobooks than watching TV or films.
4. I am good at word games like Scrabble or crosswords.
5. I like jokes and tongue twisters.
6. Other people ask me to explain the words I use when writing or speaking.
7. English is easier for me than maths.
8. In adverts I notice the words more than the pictures.
9. I often talk about things I have heard or read.
10. I have written something recently that I am proud of.

Score out of ten: _____

Picture Smart (Visual/Spatial Intelligence)

1. I often see clear pictures or images when I close my eyes.
2. Art is one of my favourite subjects.
3. I like to take pictures or videos to record what I see around me.
4. I enjoy doing jigsaw puzzles and finding my way through mazes.
5. I have vivid dreams at night.
6. I can usually find my way around places that I don't know well.
7. I like to draw or doodle.
8. I like drawing diagrams or graphs in lessons.
9. I can imagine how something would look if I was right above it.
10. I prefer books that have lots of pictures.

Score out of ten: _____

Nature Smart (Naturalistic Intelligence)

1. I like being outside.
2. I enjoy being around animals.
3. I care about the environment in which I live.
4. I can recognise many sorts of animals.
5. I can recognise many sorts of plants.
6. I recycle as much as I can.
7. I enjoy going on long walks.
8. I switch off lights to save energy.
9. I hate being stuck indoors for a long time.
10. I like the wind and the rain.

Score out of ten: _____

People Smart (Interpersonal Intelligence)

1. People often come to me for advice.
2. I prefer group sports to solo sports.
3. If I have a problem I will ask for help and not try to solve it on my own.
4. I have at least three close friends.
5. I like social games and activities rather than those I do alone.
6. I like teaching others and know how to do it.
7. I think of myself as a leader or others have called me that.
8. I feel comfortable in the middle of a crowd.
9. I like parties.
10. I prefer being in a group at night to being on my own.

Score out of ten: _____

Number/Order Smart (Logical Intelligence)

1. I can easily add and subtract numbers in my head.
2. Maths or science is my favourite subject in school.
3. I enjoy playing games and solving puzzles.
4. I like doing experiments and questioning the results.
5. I am always looking for patterns, sequences and order in things.
6. I am interested in new developments in science.
7. I sometimes solve problems in my head.
8. I always notice when people are not sensible in what they say.
9. I like it when things are measured, sorted out and put into groups.
10. I believe you can explain most things with science.

Score out of ten: _____

Myself Smart (Intrapersonal Intelligence)

1. I like to spend time alone.
2. I like lessons that help me learn more about myself.
3. I like to think for myself and not follow others.
4. I have a special hobby/interest I keep to myself.

5. I know what I want to do in the future. ❑
6. I have a good idea of my strong and weak points. ❑
7. I prefer to spend some time alone than with a crowd of people. ❑
8. I stand up for myself. ❑
9. I keep a diary to record the events in my life. ❑
10. I would like to be my own boss. ❑

Score out of ten: _____

Music Smart (Musical Intelligence)

1. I have a good singing voice. ❑
2. I can tell when someone sings or plays an instrument out of tune. ❑
3. I spend a lot of time listening to music. ❑
4. I play a musical instrument. ❑
5. My life would be boring with no music in it. ❑
6. I often cannot stop a tune running over and over in my head. ❑
7. I can keep time with a piece of music with a drum or sticks. ❑
8. I know the tunes of many different songs. ❑
9. If I hear a piece of music once or twice, I can sing it back. ❑
10. I often tap or sing a tune when I am studying or working. ❑

Score out of ten: _____

If you scored eight or above in any of the intelligences, you possess that intelligence.

WRITTEN ACTIVITY

6. Intelligences

(a) List your intelligences (i.e. the intelligences in which you scored eight or more).

_____

_____

(b) Do your goals/dreams fit with these?

_____

_____

(c) In which intelligences are you lacking?

_____

_____

(d) How might this impact on your goal-setting?

_____

_____

It is really important to understand your strengths and weaknesses when you are goal-setting. This ensures that you plan for success.

Stage Two: Reality Check

Understanding your life

In 1943, Abraham Maslow developed a hierarchy of needs. The bottom of the pyramid represents a person's basic needs and these become more advanced/complex as we move up through the levels. Look at the pyramid to decide which goals you will be focused on.

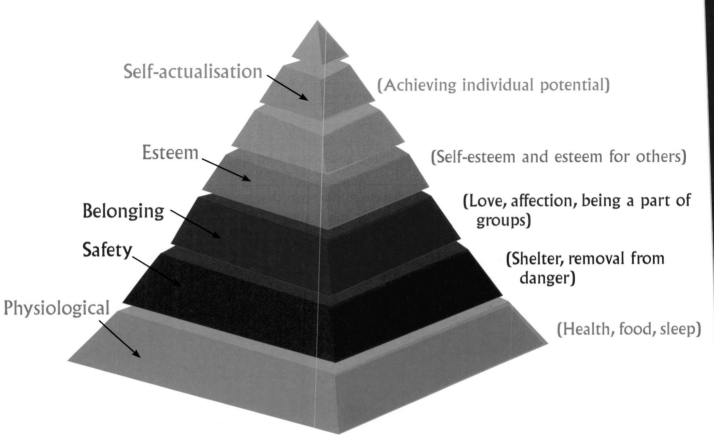

Self-actualisation — (Achieving individual potential)

Esteem — (Self-esteem and esteem for others)

Belonging — (Love, affection, being a part of groups)

Safety — (Shelter, removal from danger)

Physiological — (Health, food, sleep)

LIST ACTIVITY

7. Ten years on

Fill in the lists below. Your answers should reflect all that you hope to achieve in your life. Use Maslow's pyramid to help you reflect (a) on the needs you have fulfilled in the past 10 years and (b) how you might fulfil these and other needs in the next 10 years.

(a) Achievements in last 10 years

(i) _____

(ii) _____

(iii) _____

(iv) _____

(v) _____

(b) Achievements in next 10 years

(i) _____

(ii) _____

(iii) _____

(iv) _____

(v) _____

REFLECTION

8. What is most important to you in your life?

(a) Rank these in order. The most important thing to you is ranked as 1 and the least important is ranked as 6.

Family _____   Friends _____   Recreation _____

Career _____   Finance _____   Spiritual _____

Other _____ _____   Other _____ _____   Other _____ _____

(b) In a typical week, how much time do you spend on each?

_____

_____

_____

_____

(c) Are you spending enough time on the things and people who are most important to you?

_____

(d) Look at the list of what you hope to achieve in the next 10 years on page 15. Does this match what you have listed as most important to you?

_____

_____

The Wheel of Life

The Wheel of Life is another useful tool to help you see where you are in your life. The circle below is divided into sections representing different areas of your life. Rate your current level of satisfaction for each area on a scale of one to ten, with ten being the highest. Draw a line through each section of the wheel at the relevant point. This will give you a good visual indication of how satisfied you are with each area of your life.

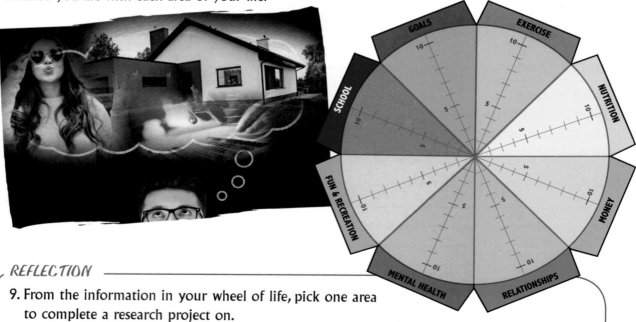

REFLECTION

9. From the information in your wheel of life, pick one area to complete a research project on.

You may find the following headings useful when completing your project:

• Future plans

• Who might help me to achieve them?

• What are my options? Who might I speak to? What information will I need to gather?

• How will I feel if my plan doesn't work out exactly as I imagined?

• How will I amend/adapt my plan?

2. Digital Wellbeing

Our world is connected through technology, so it is important to be aware of the virtual space that you can find yourself in through school, work and communications. The virtual world, in which young people spend a lot of time, is a real space and, as such, an emotion-filled space. It is vital for your wellbeing that you have the coping skills to navigate this new space.

Internet use has become an integral part of young people's everyday lives. And information and communication technologies, such as the internet and smartphones, are not just a set of tools but are environmental forces that are increasingly affecting:

- Who we are
- How we socialise
- Our conception of reality
- How we interact with reality (Floridi, 2015)

What Is Digital Wellbeing?

Enjoying digital wellbeing, means that you can look after yourself in digital spaces, that you can embrace technology to empower your relationships and work safely, and that you can appreciate a 'digital detox' every now and then (spending some time offline and device-free). It's important to be aware of the positive uses of these digital technologies in your life and also to be aware of the dangers and how you can protect yourself from being exposed to them.

THINK-PAIR-SHARE

1. Benefits and dangers of technology

(a) Can you name three ways technology benefits you on a daily basis?

(i) _____

(ii) _____

(iii) _____

(b) Can you name three ways technology could be dangerous or harmful to you?

(i) _____

(ii) _____

(iii) _____

(c) Share your results with the class. As a group, compile a list of the three most common benefits and dangers of technology.

ACTIVITY

2. Digital etiquette

Digital technologies can result in overload at work, distraction and lack of face-to-face contact with family and friends. Can you describe a time when technology distracted you from a face-to-face interaction?

_____

_____

REFLECTION

3. Look at the following situations and reflect on how you might act.

(a) You are having lunch with a group of friends. Your phone rings, and you can see it's your friend from soccer. **What do you do?**

_____

_____

_____

(b) You are helping to prepare dinner at home. You hear a message come through on your phone. **What do you do?**

_____

_____

_____

(c) You are at the cinema with your friends. One friend is texting you throughout the movie to comment on what is happening on the screen. **What do you do?**

_____

_____

_____

ACTIVITY

4. Personal Journal – mapping digital distraction

(a) For one day, record how many times you look at your phone. What prompts you to look at it? Why?

(b) Each time you check your phone, record whether you really needed to do it.

(c) As a group, work out the average amount of times phones were checked for the whole class.

Fake and Real News

HOW TO SPOT FAKE NEWS

CONSIDER THE SOURCE
Click away from the story to investigate the site, its mission and its contact info.

READ BEYOND
Headlines can be outrageous in an effort to get clicks. What's the whole story?

CHECK THE AUTHOR
Do a quick search on the author. Are they credible? Are they real?

SUPPORTING SOURCES?
Click on those links. Determine if the info given actually supports the story.

CHECK THE DATE
Reposting old news stories doesn't mean they're relevant to current events.

IS IT A JOKE?
If it is too outlandish, it might be satire. Research the site and author to be sure.

CHECK YOUR BIASES
Consider if your own beliefs could affect your judgement.

ASK THE EXPERTS
Ask a librarian, or consult a fact-checking site.

IFLA
International Federation of Library Associations and Institutions

Critical thinking

Newspaper headlines might be an old-fashioned way of finding information or news, but how do we decide the value we place on these headlines? How do we know whether or not to trust the source? What can we use to assess the information?

The information in the infographic on the left can help you recognise false or misleading stories by checking the credibilty of the source or the author.

THINK-PAIR-SHARE

5. Trusted Sources

(a) Name five sources of news that you believe provide accurate and truthful information.

(i) _____

(ii) _____

(iii) _____

(iv) _____

(v) _____

(b) Share your list with your partner and discuss why you trust the information from these sources.

(i) _____

(ii) _____

(iii) _____

(c) Why do you think some media sources might give false or inaccurate information?

(i) _____

(ii) _____

(iii) _____

Digital natives

Those born after 1995 are sometimes called Generation Z and are often referred to as **digital natives**. These are people who have grown up using technology and are believed to have a better understanding of digital technology than those who have been born earlier. However, the OECD (Organisation for Economic Cooperation and Development) (2015) showed that while digital natives could use technology, they did not critically engage with it and its impacts.

A 2016 Irish study investigating how students act and think about technology supports the OECD's work, finding that digital natives do not know how to use digital media safely. It looked at seven key issues with the digital literacy and digital wellbeing of Irish adolescents:

	Questions asked	What the students said
1.	Do you feel safer online or face to face?	Feel safer online
2.	What is the impact of being hurt by technology?	Death, self-harm
3.	What apps are frequently used by students?	Snapchat
4.	What are the best things about technology?	Connectivity, pornography, anonymity
5.	What are the worst things about technology?	Cyber-bullying, dangerous, addictive
6.	What are the skills of someone who is good with technology?	Hacking, developing software, making lots of money
7.	Is there an unwritten phone/device etiquette?	Yes. We all know each other's PIN but would never look at Snapchat or photos on another person's phone

One of the most striking findings of the survey was that a very high percentage of people – 66% – knew someone who had been hurt by the misuse of technology.

REFLECTION

6 . Technology misuse

(a) Do you know of anyone who was hurt by the misuse of technology?

_____

_____

_____

(b) How do you think they could have prevented themselves from being hurt on line?

_____

_____

_____

(c) Do you know how to protect your online data?

_____

_____

_____

(d) Do you know what your privacy settings are on your devices (phone, tablet etc.)?

_____

_____

_____

(e) If you were hurt by someone on line, what would you do? Who would you tell?

_____

_____

_____

NOTE

Remember your one good adult,
someone you can talk to and whose advice you can trust.

3. Self-Management: A Sense of Purpose

So far, in this module, you have spent some time understanding yourself on a personal level, and also your real and digital lives. In the next section, you will look at ways you can manage yourself.

Working in Groups

In this section you will explore how to work in groups. You will also consider the rights and responsibilities of each person in a group and ways of respecting each other.

GROUP ACTIVITY

1. Imagine that you have to organise a soccer tournament for 30 Sixth Class pupils from the local primary school. The event is on in two weeks' time and will last for three hours.
   In a group, create a plan for this activity and present it to the rest of the class.

WRITTEN ACTIVITY

2. Review

(a) What steps did the group take to create the plan?

_____

_____

(b) What contribution did you make to the task?

_____

_____

(c) How did you feel working in your group?

_____

_____

(d) Why did you feel this way?

_____

_____

(e) If you had to do the same task again, would you behave differently?

_____

_____

(f) Did you feel that your group was productive? Give a reason for your answer.

_____

_____

(g) How should group members behave when working on a task?

_____

_____

Helpful keywords

Leadership	Communication skills	Aggressive	Helpful	Passive	Assertive
Team player	Committed	Constructive	Respectful		

Rights and Responsibilities

In order to work effectively in a group the rights of each person must be respected. But what exactly are rights?

Every person (parent, student, teacher etc.) has rights and these rights are linked to their individual needs.

It is important to remember, however, that every right brings with it a responsibility, e.g. I have the right to be safe and I also have the responsibility to make sure I do not interfere with the safety of others. In other words, my actions should not interfere with the rights of others. Every individual's rights are recognised in the Universal Declaration of Human Rights (UDHR). It is important to remember to practise these rights at all times.

GROUP ACTIVITY

3. As a group, list five basic rights you believe every human being should have.

TABLE ACTIVITY

4. In the columns below list three rights you and your classmates identified and the responsibilities associated with each right.

Rights	Responsibilities
(a)	
(b)	
(c)	

Throughout our lives we will encounter various rules as students, workers, friends and citizens and we have a responsibility to follow these rules. Young children may not understand all the rules but as we grow older and have more life experiences, we can begin to understand the consequences of not following rules.

Every action has a reaction and we are responsible for that. For example, it is illegal for a person to drive a car in Ireland unless they have a driving licence and a certain amount of experience. So if a 16-year-old decides to drive a car without a licence, she/he will have to deal with the consequences.

There are usually penalties associated with breaking the law. As with all rules and guidelines, conflict may arise when people disagree over the consequences of breaking some laws, e.g. the death penalty in America. This type of conflict is explored in a novel called *Lord of the Flies* by William Golding in which a group of children are stranded on a desert island and have to develop rules to ensure they survive. They begin with a civilised structure but order breaks down when rules are no longer followed and chaos ensues.

'I must do something' always solves more problems than 'Something must be done'.
Anonymous

No man was ever endowed with a right without being at the same time saddled with a responsibility.
Gerald W. Johnson, American historian and novelist

We have not passed that subtle line between childhood and adulthood until we have stopped saying 'It got lost' and say 'I lost it'.
Sidney J. Harris, American journalist

TABLE ACTIVITY

5. In the space below identify rules which are expected to be followed and the consequences of not following them.

Person	Rule	Consequences of breaking rule
Student	Must attend school until 16 years of age	Perform poorly in exams, parents may be prosecuted
Worker		
Friend		
Citizen		
Parent		
Teacher		

GROUP ACTIVITY

6. Discuss the statement 'Rules are made to be broken'.

RESEARCH

7. Read *Lord of the Flies* by William Golding and identify the importance of rules and responsibilities in the book.

Rules

Rules are put in place to ensure that a person's rights are protected.

CLASS CHARTER

8. Draw up a list of ten rules to make a Class Charter to protect the rights of every person in your class (including your teacher). You can do this on your own or in small groups.

(a) _____

(b) _____

(c) _____

(d) _____

(e) _____

(f) _____

(g) _____

(h) _____

(i) _____

(j) _____

Manners

Manners are a sensitive awareness of the feelings of others. If you have that awareness, you have good manners, no matter which fork you use.
Emily Post, American author on etiquette (i.e. manners)

Friends and good manners will carry you where money won't go.
Margaret Walker, American poet

Do manners matter?

Within society manners change from generation to generation. Did you know a handshake was originally used as a way of showing that a man wasn't carrying a sword or dagger in his hand?

Manners today still exist although maybe in different forms. The underlying concepts of manners are (1) custom (2) consideration and (3) common sense.

WRITTEN ACTIVITY

9. Good Manners

(a) **Custom** is the habit of doing something in a particular situation. List some habits which people do in particular situations, e.g. shaking hands when you meet someone new.

_____

_____

_____

(b) **Consideration** is one of the most important parts of having manners. Having consideration for someone else shows you care and are concerned for the other person's feelings.
Give some examples of when you might be considerate in a social situation.

_____

_____

_____

(c) **Common sense:** Nearly all manners require an element of common sense.
Think of some situations in which common sense is needed.

_____

_____

_____

In different areas of our life we have certain manners which are appropriate.

TABLE ACTIVITY

10. Give an example of appropriate and inappropriate behaviour in each of the following situations.

	Appropriate	**Inappropriate**
Manners at home	**Finish eating before you speak**	**Speaking with your mouth full**
Manners at school		
Phone manners		
Being a guest		
Manners when you are out and about		
Manners and body language		
Manners and communication - speaking, messaging, online, written		

For teenagers to be successful in life, they need to have social skills (skills used to interact and communicate with other people effectively) as well as academic skills. If you practise polite and caring behaviour and use good manners, you will become more socially aware as you grow older.

People displaying bad manners have 'a profound sense of entitlement, a disregard for the needs of others, and an inability to put forth the genuine effort needed to develop — academically, socially, and emotionally.' Madeline Levine, American psychologist

Common courtesy

- Always say please and thank you — good manners show you care about others
- Don't talk or text on your phone when someone is trying to talk to you
- Avoid bad language — particularly when talking to adults or when young children are around
- Hold doors for people coming behind you
- Be aware of those around you and help anyone who might need assistance

Impress Your Elders

Older generations often feel that younger people don't maintain the same standards of politeness that they learned in their youth. Encounters with rude teenagers will just reinforce this belief. Show them they've got it wrong by being on your best behaviour around them. Make eye contact with adults and shake their hand firmly when introduced. Listen to them and respect their experience, even if you think they can't understand your experiences. You may find you have more in common than you realise!

Influence Your Peers

Set a good example for your friends by having good manners — you may find they pick them up too. If a friend is being rude, politely point out that they should treat people as they would like to be treated.

Table Manners

Entertaining clients at restaurants can be an important part of business — and older clients are less than impressed with young executives who don't have proper table manners. Some companies are sending their younger employees to dining etiquette coaches to learn how to eat certain foods and how to use cutlery properly before allowing them to take clients to dinner. Increasingly, job interviews are being held over meals, so interviewers can observe how interviewees behave in a restaurant setting. So simple dining manners could be the difference between being offered your dream job or being left behind.

GROUP ACTIVITY

11. In small groups, discuss how the use of manners can help you to attain the following characteristics:

Resilience
Perseverance
Consideration
for others
SPORTSMANSHIP
Respect
Patience
GENEROSITY

GROUP ACTIVITY

12. Get Creative

(a) Find an inspirational quote (or quotes) — sayings that move or inspire you — about manners and respect. Display it (or them) as posters around the school.

(b) Create a Manners Certificate for Junior Cert students. Ask teachers in your school to nominate students for random acts of good manners observed throughout the school year. An awards ceremony can be made at the students' assembly or the students can be recognised over the school intercom.

(c) Organise a poetry/essay/poster competition to highlight the importance of manners in your school.
Remember to 'Practise what you Preach' and use your manners!

To live is to choose. But to choose well, you must know who you are and what you stand for, where you want to go and why you want to get there.

We may have different religions, different languages, different coloured skin, but we all belong to one human race.
Kofi Annan, Ghanaian diplomat, seventh secretary-general of the United Nations, winner of the 2001 Nobel Peace Prize.

Study Skills

Now that you have created your Class Charter, and looked at ways to work better with others and how to behave well in company, next we will explore how you can optimise your time in senior cycle to achieve your goals and dreams. With this in mind, this section looks at:

(a) Organising My Time   **(b)** Planning for Effective Study   **(c)** Coping with Examinations

(a) Organising My Time

TABLE ACTIVITY

13. It is important to organise your time well so that you can spend it effectively. In the timetable below fill in how much time you spend each day on activities. Total the time spent each day and then each week on each activity. How balanced is your life?

	Mon	Tues	Wed	Thur	Fri	Sat	Sun	Weekly Total
School								
Homework								
Study								
Afterschool Activities								
Entertainment online (music, videos)								
Gaming								
Sports								
Phone								
Meeting Friends								
Eating								
Sleeping								
Part-Time Work								
Messaging								

There are 24 hours in the day. You spend eight hours sleeping, two hours eating, seven hours at school and perhaps two or three hours on homework. That leaves about four hours for other activities! So choose well. Getting the best from your day is all about organising your time.

(b) Planning for Effective Study

Studying can be seen as a strategy towards self-improvement. It can certainly strengthen your chances in an exam situation as well as pave the way for future learning. Planning for effective study really depends on students' attitudes.

By shifting your mindset from passive to positive, you stand a better chance of overcoming the fear of even starting to study. You need to find out what works best for you. Here are some guidelines to help you get started.

Passive = lacking in energy or will

1. Think positive.

Think of the athlete who wins the race. What makes that athlete a winner is their Positive Mental Attitude. How well you believe in yourself will make the difference. Apparently we mentally talk to ourselves thousands of times a day. Try turning some of that self-chat into positive statements such as, 'I can do it'. That, in itself, is a good start.

I am the greatest. I said that even before I knew I was.

2. Memory tips

How do we remember things?

We have two types of memory. Depending on what we are learning, we store the information in one of these two types of memory.

- Short-Term Memory (STM) = This will hold information for 15 seconds if it is not transferred into the long-term memory.

If we repeat words / sentences over and over, it can be transferred into:

- Long-Term Memory (LTM) = This will hold information over a longer period, e.g. hours, days, weeks, years.

3. Aids to learning

(a) Make a connection: Try to make links between new information and stored information. When you are learning, your brain needs to encode the information so it can be stored in memory.

(b) Encoding: This is the way information is changed in your brain so that you can store it (e.g. through repetition or breaking information up into small sections, such as learning one verse of a poem at a time).

(c) Spread out your learning time: Cramming does not really work — you will only remember the information for about an hour or two.

(d) Use rhymes, mnemonics and stories to help you create meaning for information. Mnemonics are good if you have to learn a list, e.g. ROY G. BIV = colours of the rainbow.

Mnemonics = Creating meaningless connections for information to help memory retrieval. It is pronounced 'Neh-moniks'.

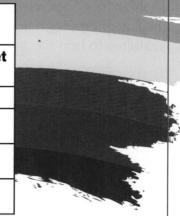

TABLE ACTIVITY

14. Can you think of a list to make a mnemonic?

Subject 1	Science: Colours of the rainbow
List	Red, Orange, Yellow, Green, Blue, Indigo, Violet
Mnemonic	Roy G.Biv
Subject 2	
List	
Mnemonic	

Learning studying skills

Developing studying skills means building good habits. Here are some suggestions.

1. Read the information first, a couple of times if necessary.
2. Divide the information into smaller sections.
3. Read the smaller sections to check you understand what is being said.
4. Write the information in your own words or in point form.
5. If the exam involves a considerable amount of text, e.g. History or English, try learning the smaller paragraphs one at a time.
6. Recall the information by testing yourself.
7. Maybe write a question or two for each section you are learning.
8. Remember the key words to help you recall information.
9. Decide whether you know the information:
    (a) Perfectly
    (b) Enough to get by
    (c) Not at all

(c) Coping with Examinations

Understanding terms

When we don't understand the question, it is difficult to provide an answer. Some words used in exam questions and their explanations are listed below.

Enumerate/List/State	**List the points, no descriptions are necessary.**
Characteristics	**List the qualities of a person/place/thing.**
Properties	**List the features of a substance, e.g. fat, soluble etc.**
Define	**Write down the precise meaning of a word or phrase. In some cases it may be necessary to give an example or very brief description.**
Select/Name/Suggest	**State the answer in one or two words. There is no need for detail.**
Outline	**Write one or two sentences on each point, i.e. give a brief description.**
Describe	**Give a written description in point form. Use a diagram to back up your answer if applicable.**
Explain	**Give a detailed account, back up your answer with a specific example and include a diagram if applicable.**
Discuss/Give an account of	**This requires a very detailed description of what is being asked. Remember to structure your answer in point form. Provide at least six points in your answer unless otherwise stated.**
Informative paragraph	**Provide at least five points in your answer and structure it in point form.**
Classify	**Group the items into categories.**
Evaluate	**Make an assessment of the worth of something – could be referring to negative and positive uses etc.**
Illustrate	**Make something clear by the use of concrete examples, e.g. diagrams to explain or clarify a point.**

RESEARCH

15. Some subjects have special words that are used in exam situations.

   Find a subject that uses such words in questions; remember, you might have more than one word for each subject.

Subject	Word	Meaning
Home Economics	**Dietetic**	**The role the particular food has in the diet**

Your school is there to help you. Ask your teacher to explain things further for you. Don't be afraid to get more help if needed from the school's career guidance and counselling team. It is best to ask for help as soon as you can to avoid falling behind or becoming completely lost in a subject.

> *I hated every minute of training, but I said, 'Don't quit. Suffer now and live the rest of your life as a champion.'* Muhammad Ali

PLANNING

16. In your copy or on a blank sheet, make out a time plan for your revision for Christmas exams or Mocks/Pres or summer exams or for your Leaving Certificate/Leaving Certificate Applied exams.

Relaxation

The 4 Rs: Revise, Review, Remember, Relax

How to Relax

One definition of relaxing is 'to make less tense or rigid or to become looser or less rigid' [Collins Dictionary].

During Senior Cycle, it is important that you take time to relax. Take some time away from your studies to spend with friends, on hobbies, listening to music, reading and/or exercising.

LIST ACTIVITY

17. List the activities you would most like to spend time on (think of Maslow's pyramid on page 15):

(a) _____

(b) _____

(c) _____

(d) _____

(e) _____

(f) _____

Many students become anxious and feel they cannot get all of their homework and revision completed. By planning and organising, you can get all the necessary work finished and then ... relax.

WRITTEN ACTIVITY

18. Relaxation methods

(a) List three methods you could use to relax.

(i) _____

(ii) _____

(iii) _____

(b) How important is it to relax?

_____

_____

_____

(c) Are there any other methods you could use to help you relax? Maybe you can share some ideas with the person sitting next to you.

Active

10 steps to relaxation

This exercise can be done in school or at home. It helps if you play gentle music in the background. Allow 15 to 20 minutes for this exercise. Try it at least once and see how you feel.

1. Sit in a quiet room with soft gentle background music playing or incense burning. (Remember fire safety when using matches or candles.)
2. Place feet flat on the ground. Remove your shoes first if you want. Alternatively, lay down on a mat on the floor.
3. Breathe slowly and deeply — iiiiinnn oooouuut. Listen to your breathing and close your eyes.
4. Concentrate on your breathing — in and out.
5. Now very slowly tense your toes and feet and hold for ten seconds.
6. Relax.
7. Repeat Steps 5 and 6 for all parts of your body — legs, back, stomach, hands, arms, shoulders, neck and face.
8. When you have completed all the steps above, your body should feel relaxed and free of any tension.
9. Continue listening to the music/silence.
10. When you are ready, open your eyes slowly and sit up.

TABLE ACTIVITY

19. Fill in the table below to make a plan for relaxing during your exams.

	Mon	Tue	Wed	Thurs	Fri	Sat	Sun
Time spent relaxing							
Way of relaxing							

While relaxation is healthy, it is vital to ensure you also eat a balanced diet and have adequate exercise. This will be explained in more detail in **Module 6: Physical Activity and Nutrition**. Be sure to:

- Eat your breakfast, drink plenty of water and bring some water into the exam centre with you.
- Eat plenty of vegetables, reduce your caffeine intake (e.g. tea, coffee, cola) and avoid fatty food.

4. Your Life Plan: How Has It Changed?

PERSONALITY TYPE

1. Circle your personality type below. You identified this already in the Life Plan at the beginning of the book.

2. Your personality can directly impact how you understand, accept or reject some of the concepts in this module. What changes or challenges are ahead of you?

_____

_____

_____

3. How might you learn to deal with these changes or challenges? Think of your multiple intelligences. These may offer clues as to how you may best approach these changes or challenges.

_____

_____

_____

REALITY CHECK

4. Thinking about what we've explored in this module, fill out your Wheel of Life again.

(a) Has anything changed? Y ☐ N ☐
(b) If so, what has changed and why?

_____

_____

_____

(c) Do you need to take action in any area? Y ☐ N ☐
(d) If so, what actions do you need to take?

_____

_____

_____

(e) Identify who might help you achieve these actions.

_____

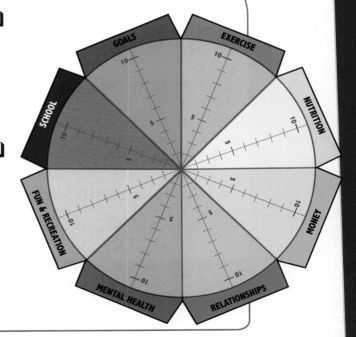

GOALS

5. Do you need to set a goal for this area in your life? If so, go to page 223 for a Goal Worksheet.

Module 2: Mental Health

1. Physical, Emotional and Social Aspects of Mental Health

ACTIVITY

1. If you had to write a definition of mental health, what would it be?

Mental health is _____

_____

_____

Definition of Mental Health

* A state of emotional and social wellbeing in which the individual can cope with the normal stresses of life and achieve his or her potential.
* It includes being able to work productively and contribute to community life.
* Mental health describes the ability of individuals and groups to interact, inclusively and equitably (fairly), with one another and with their environment in ways that encourage subjective wellbeing and increase opportunities for development and the use of mental abilities.
* Mental health is not simply the absence of mental illness.

Health is a complete state of physical, mental and social well-being, not just the absence of disease or infirmity. World Health Organisation

Mental Health

Mental health is influenced by our physical wellbeing so how we look after and care for our bodies and the choice of foods we make can all impact on how we feel about ourselves.

Ultimately mental health is how we feel about ourselves, those around us and how we cope with demands that are placed on us. Remember, everybody at some stage in their life is going to be faced with challenges, some more than others, so it is important to know how you will react and cope with situations.

Remember:
It isn't the number of situations you are exposed to, but how you perceive and interpret them.

REFLECTION

2. From reading the definitions on the previous page, identify the common misconceptions you have heard or had about mental health.

_____

_____

_____

_____

_____

_____

_____

_____

_____

_____

_____

_____

_____

_____

_____

_____

_____

_____

RESEARCH

In some parts of the media a stigma can be attached to someone who needs treatment for mental health challenges. However if the same person needed medical assistance for a broken leg the media hype surrounding it would be much less. It is important we realise that our mental health is one area of our health that needs to be maintained and nurtured.

In your opinion how do the media portray celebrities who may be trying to overcome mental health issues? Collect stories on celebrities who have overcome mental health challenges.

J. K. Rowling, Prince Harry and Demi Lovato have all spoken publicly about their mental health issues.

2. Self-Awareness and Personal Skills

The Emotional Coping Brain

If mothers didn't have an emotional brain, they wouldn't feel the instinct to nurture and feed their young. The emotional part of our brain is the link with our thinking brain (neocortex) which allows us to know and name what we are feeling, e.g. happiness, sadness etc. The words 'emotions' and 'feelings' are often used interchangeably. However the emotional experience and feelings are different. We have an emotional experience, e.g. having a fun time with friends; however our feelings go beyond that. Feelings result from our emotional brain's reaction to what we are experiencing.

Feelings can be seen as the internal interpretation of our emotional experiences. Two people can experience the same stressful situation but their inner interpretation will be determined by their own neocortex, which will give meaning to the situation and decide the best way to react/cope with it. One person may be sad and cry; the other person may not.

The emotional coping brain has three elements:
1. Thinking (neocortex – logical)
2. Emotional (mammalian – instinctive)
3. Reptilian (survival and instinctive)

Our **reptilian impulse** is very quick and may be anger or avoidance, whereas the **thinking** brain will take a while to decide how we are feeling and what to do about it.

Neuroscientists refer to this emotional function as the limbic system.

WRITTEN ACTIVITY

1. Positivity

 (a) *"The fundamental goal of positive education is to promote flourishing or positive mental health within the school community."* (Norrish et. al., 2013)

 (i) What does this mean to you?

 _____

 _____

 _____

 (ii) How can you apply this to your own mental health?

 _____

 _____

 _____

(b) "Compared to unhappy students, happier students pay better attention, are more creative, and have greater levels of community involvement. The emphasis on positive psychology interventions in education increases engagement, creates more curious students, and helps develop an overall love of learning." (Fisher, 2015)

(i) What does this mean to you?

_____

_____

_____

(ii) How can you apply this to your own mental health?

_____

_____

_____

Constructive Self-Talk

Constructive self-talk is a way of responding and coping when faced with a difficult situation. In simple words, it's the internal dialogue that we have within ourselves. If you think about it, we have a continuous internal dialogue with ourselves. This dialogue can be constructive but likewise it can be deconstructive. Sometimes it can be what someone else has said to us (e.g. 'you're stupid' or 'you're fat') rather than something we have thought of ourselves. Everyone has this internal dialogue and it's important to know how to use it as a coping skill. We judge others and ourselves, we argue, we praise and we label. Often this can be done within ourselves.

> Another name for constructive self-talk is **affirmation**.

Learned Optimism

It is possible to retrain your way of thinking so you can be more optimistic when faced with life's challenges. Ask yourself the following questions:
1. When things don't work out for you, what do you do or what can you do?
2. Do you think you are the cause of the problem / situation?
3. Do you often think that a problem is because of something you did?
4. Do you feel like a victim?

It's time to reframe. Psychologists Reivich and Shatte devised the **Resilience Factor** (2002):
If something goes wrong consider the following . . .
1. Look for alternatives.
2. Look at the evidence presented.
3. Consider the implications.

If you can do this, you will be more optimistic about future situations that don't work out as well as you had planned.

WRITTEN ACTIVITY

2. Read the following stories and apply the three Resilience Factors to each situation.

(a) Rory has been playing with the local hurling club. He is very disappointed that he hasn't been picked for the team in the upcoming finals. He feels he isn't good enough although he never misses training and has played in most of the games so far this year until he had a hamstring injury. Rory isn't feeling too good about himself at the moment. Help him construct some positive self-talk.

(i)   Look for alternatives.

_____

_____

_____

(ii)   Look at the evidence presented.

_____

_____

_____

(iii) Consider the implications.

_____

_____

_____

(b) Alex was really looking forward to going to the concert in Dublin with her friends, but now she can't go, as her granny has been taken ill. Alex must stay at home to look after her younger brother while her parents go to look after her granny. Alex feels life is so unfair and she deserved to go to the concert because she has been working all summer and saving her money. If you were Alex's friend how would you help her construct positive self-talk?

(i)   Look for alternatives.

_____

_____

(ii)   Look at the evidence presented.

_____

_____

_____

(iii) Consider the implications.

_____

_____

(c) Rebecca thinks she is unattractive, overweight and stupid. Rebecca's friends don't understand why she feels this way but ever since Rebecca can remember her brother told her she was fat and ugly and stupid. Her friends really want to help her. What can they do and say to help Rebecca?

(i) Look for alternatives.

_____

_____

_____

(ii) Look at the evidence presented.

_____

_____

_____

(iii) Consider the implications.

_____

_____

_____

Resilience – What It Means

Throughout our lives we are faced with difficulties. It is important to have the resilience and coping skills to help us during these times. Resilience will help us bounce back and search for new opportunities.

Research has shown that resilient people tend to:
- Be happier
- Live longer
- Be more successful in school or at work
- Be happier in relationships
- Be less prone to depression

(Reivich & Shatte 2002; Werner & Smith 2001)

It is how we think about our difficulties or hardship (adversity) which will cause our feelings and contribute to our behaviour.

How can I become more resilient?

If you change the way you think about adversity and opportunity, then it is possible to learn how to be a more resilient person. As with all new skills it takes time and practice, but it will eventually change the way you respond to or think about situations. This resilience will be vital if you ever have to overcome the negativity of others, either through words or actions. In school, at work, with friends etc. we will meet people who may be negative towards us and it is here we can use our skills of resilience and not let the actions or the words of someone else overcome us.

> Resilience is an ongoing process.

In becoming more resilient it is important to be focused and stay calm in situations and look at and create alternatives (remember there are always alternatives even if initially you feel something isn't right for you). Sometimes it may be necessary to challenge our beliefs or those of people around us.

Coping Styles

Each individual will have a different way of responding to a stressful situation. Coping has been defined as 'the person's cognitive and behavioural efforts to manage specific external or internal demands that are appraised as taxing or exceeding the resources of the person' (Folkman and Lazarus, 1988).

Coping involves assessing the different thought processes and behaviours we engage in to try and deal with the stressful situation.

The COPE Scale which was devised by Carver, Scheier and Weintraub (1989) is one way of identifying how you manage stressful situations. This scale has been modified by many psychologists over the years, some of whom introduced subscales.

> A subscale is an addition to the original scale.

COPE Subscales

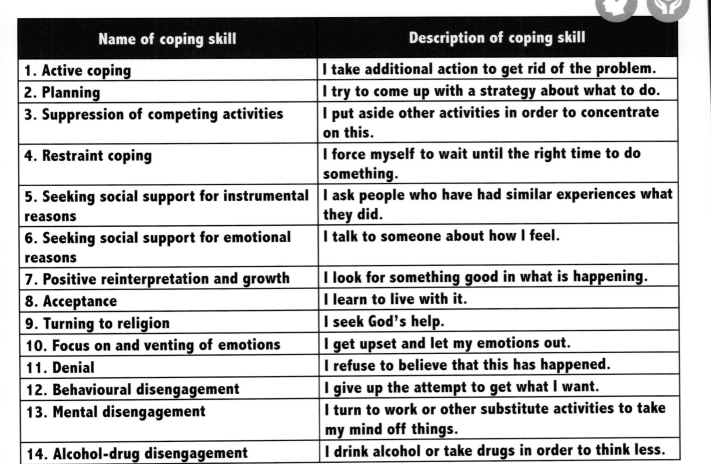

Name of coping skill	Description of coping skill
1. Active coping	I take additional action to get rid of the problem.
2. Planning	I try to come up with a strategy about what to do.
3. Suppression of competing activities	I put aside other activities in order to concentrate on this.
4. Restraint coping	I force myself to wait until the right time to do something.
5. Seeking social support for instrumental reasons	I ask people who have had similar experiences what they did.
6. Seeking social support for emotional reasons	I talk to someone about how I feel.
7. Positive reinterpretation and growth	I look for something good in what is happening.
8. Acceptance	I learn to live with it.
9. Turning to religion	I seek God's help.
10. Focus on and venting of emotions	I get upset and let my emotions out.
11. Denial	I refuse to believe that this has happened.
12. Behavioural disengagement	I give up the attempt to get what I want.
13. Mental disengagement	I turn to work or other substitute activities to take my mind off things.
14. Alcohol-drug disengagement	I drink alcohol or take drugs in order to think less.

(Marks, Murray, Evans, Willig, 2000)

If you look at the list you will probably realise that you use a number of the coping mechanisms mentioned above. However if your choice of coping mechanism is detrimental to your overall wellbeing, it might be a good idea to pick another one and start using that instead.

Link Up
See also Module 4,
Substance Use, page 89

Who wants praise?

Let's face it, we all love to be praised and thanked. Throughout our lives it helps to receive praise from various people, e.g. parents, family, friends, schoolteachers, coaches etc. Take a minute to think of the last time you were praised or praised someone else. How did that feel?

Can you distinguish between the different types of praise in the statements on the right?

You're very smart and clever

You researched that project well.

- ✐ The first statement is **person praise** as you are praising the person.
- ✐ The second one is **process praise** as you are praising the achievement.

Kamins and Dweck (1999) identified process praise and person praise and found that children who received **person praise** displayed the following:

1. Greater difficulty in dealing with stressful situations.
2. Lower performing skills.
3. Less persistence.
4. Tendency to pick easier tasks so as not to lose the label.

Children who received **process praise**:

1. were better able to cope with difficult situations
2. had more enjoyment
3. were more persistent
4. picked harder tasks when given a choice, as they didn't have a label to preserve.

If a child is learning to do something new and is told 'good boy' when he gets it right, does this imply that he is a bad boy when he makes a mistake? Person praise would indicate this is what happens internally.

WRITTEN ACTIVITY

3. **Think of a piece of homework that you submitted to a teacher.** Write a note about the work, from the teacher's point of view, that you as a student would find meaningful and helpful.

Does the colour of the pen used affect how you feel about the written praise?

_____

_____

_____

_____

_____

_____

_____

The Positive Diary

It is believed that people remember good things or accomplishments for longer if they share them with others (Gable et al., 2004).

For the next week keep a diary and write down your judgemental self-talk. If you find yourself being critical, reframe it and make it more event specific and look at alternatives to the situation. Highlight your self-praise but analyse it and make it process praise as opposed to person praise.

Finally, don't forget to share your accomplishments with others, e.g. a parent friend or your one good adult.

3. Emotional Health

Emotions and feelings are two different things. You may feel lonely or rejected and you express that feeling through the emotion, whatever that may be, e.g. anger.

What is emotional health about?

Emotional health is the ability to express all our emotions appropriately. It is the way we feel and how we feel about others; it is part of our overall wellbeing. It is being able to recognise and acknowledge our own emotions and respect those of the people around us. We may not always feel the same as others. We develop skills and through life experiences build up our emotional wellbeing. Once we feel and acknowledge an emotion, it changes. Hence the emotion.

Why is emotional health important for us?

Having good emotional health and social skills can help ensure we have a happy and contented life. It ensures success at school, at work and in relationships. Spending too much time on video games etc. limits your ability to create social skills.

Often people who don't socialise have a greater risk of depression and suicidal thoughts. In many societies today teenage self-harm is very prevalent. Teenagers who self-harm don't yet have appropriate coping skills and often don't know how to ask for help or where to go for help.

What is self-harm?

This is when a person deliberately hurts or injures themselves by cutting or burning themselves, overdosing on drugs, driving excessively fast or tearing and scratching skin. If you are self-harming or you know someone who is, please turn to an adult you trust for help.

How to Look after Your Emotional Health

🖎 Spend time with loved ones — family and friends.

🖎 Engage in physical activities, competitive or non-competitive (see **Module 6: Physical Activity and Nutrition**).

🖎 Be self-aware: Know yourself and what can make you react in certain ways.

🖎 Keep a healthy balance between work and play.

🖎 Keep physically healthy through what you eat.

🖎 Do something or be involved in a positive action, e.g. helping a charity.

REFLECTION

1. Emotional Reactions

(a) Can you list five emotions that you clearly remember and the situations that caused you to feel that way (e.g. anger because roadworks caused your bus to be late arriving to your school)?

Emotion	Cause
1.	
2.	
3.	
4.	
5.	

(b) When you look back at the list how would you deal with these situations now? Would your reaction be the same? If not, why?

_____

_____

_____

_____

_____

_____

4. Stress Management

What Is Stress?

Stress refers to a process in which some event occurs in your life (the stressor) with which you fear you do not have the ability to cope (Brace and Westcott, 2002).

The concept of stress is part of our everyday lives and stress becomes an issue for us when we don't know how to cope with it. Think about a young child who loses their mother in a shopping centre: this will cause huge distress for the child until they are reunited with their parent. However if the same situation happened to a 14-year-old the level of stress would be greatly reduced as they would have a coping strategy to deal with such a situation.

> Stress is an individual response to an inappropriate level of pressure. It is the response to pressure, not the pressure itself.
> (Arroba and James 1987)

WRITTEN ACTIVITY

1. In the space below describe three things that are causing you stress in your life at the moment.

(a) _____
_____
_____
_____
_____

(b) _____
_____
_____
_____
_____

(c) _____
_____
_____
_____
_____

When you look back at your list you might find that relationships with others can cause the greatest amount of stress in our lives. What relationships might cause you to be stressed?

Remember it is not possible to eliminate all aspects of stress from our lives so it is important that we develop ways of dealing with a stressful situation. Stress can be present for a short length of time, e.g. before you play a match or go into an exam, or stress can be more long-term and impact greatly on your life.

Stress, if not treated and managed, can result in serious health problems, e.g. high blood pressure, ulcers, anxiety attacks.

The Three Dimensions of Stress

2. Coping Skills — The skills and strategies that we use to deal with pressure and manage stressful situations.

1. Stressors — Situations which produce pressure for us and are therefore potential sources of stress.

3. Support — Knowing the possible sources of support including formal and informal support (e.g. family and friends).

Remember your one good adult, someone you can talk to and whose advice you can trust.

Coping Measures

1. **Play a sport; Go for a run; Read a book; Write a poem/story; Go for a walk**

2. **Call a friend; Confide in a family member; Visit a spiritual place**

3. **Meditate; Say a prayer; Joke or laugh; Play computer games; Listen to music; Prioritise; Watch TV; Ask for help; Think positively; Moan; Clean up; Do something**

Link up
See also Coping Styles on page 43

WRITTEN ACTIVITY

2. Coping with Stress

(a) How do I feel when I am stressed?

_____

_____

_____

(b) What do I do?

_____

_____

_____

(c) What works well for me?

_____

_____

_____

GROUP ACTIVITY

As a class group make a school charter on how to manage stress. Use this charter during health promotion week or put it on your school web page.

When we cope with stress we develop strategies which help us. It is important that we have a few strategies rather than depending on just one. When we combine different strategies (e.g. exercise and talking to someone), we generally will have more positive thoughts and feel less stressed.

You will realise from the list that some coping strategies come from within ourselves (e.g. positive thinking, listening to music, yoga) and some come from other people (e.g. talking to someone, socialising).

How Do I know if I'm stressed?

It is important to remember that each person will respond differently to a situation. For one person an experience could be extremely stressful but for another it could be very enjoyable, e.g. travelling on a plane. However our response to stress can be divided into three categories:

- Physical
- Behavioural
- Psychological

LIST ACTIVITY

3. **Place the symptoms of stress into one of the boxes below.** Maybe you can identify with some of the symptoms listed.

Symptoms of Stress		
Increased breathing and heart rate,	Gritting or grinding of teeth,	Difficulty making decisions,
Nervousness,	Tense muscles,	A sense of being overloaded or over-burdened by problems,
Irritable,	Finger or foot-tapping,	
Anxious,	Blushing,	Edginess,
Tense,	Diarrhoea or constipation,	Panic attacks,
Butterflies in stomach,	Fatigue,	Increased use of alcohol or cigarettes,
Tearful,	Worry,	
Nightmares,	Guilt or nervousness,	Changes in eating patterns,
Anger,		
Aches and Pains,	Frustration,	Defensiveness or suspicion,
A dry mouth,	Depression,	
Clammy hands,	Racing thoughts,	Withdrawal from social situations.
Difficulty sleeping,	Problems in concentrating or learning,	
Tension headaches,		

Physical	**Behavioural**	**Psychological**

One survey said that the top 10 causes of stress in our everyday lives are:

1. Death of a spouse or close relative
2. Divorce
3. Personal injury or illness
4. Marriage
5. Work redundancy
6. Retirement
7. Change in health of family member
8. Pregnancy
9. Sexual problems
10. Change in financial state

Source: www.halfaloaf.ie

REFLECTION

4. Can you identify the reasons why a person might become stressed in three of the situations listed on the bottom of the previous page? What coping strategies would you recommend and why?

Cause	Stress	Strategies

Workplace and Stress

Over the coming years you will be moving onto another phase of your life: going to college, travelling and working. These new changes can bring with them other potential forms of stress in your life so it is important to remember the coping skills discussed earlier.

However one of the coping strategies that can be learned and used by everyone is your **emotional intelligence.**

☺ To be self-aware – know your emotions and the impact they can have on you, e.g. know what makes you angry or annoyed and how you will react.

☺ To self-manage – control our emotions and behaviour, e.g. to know what is socially acceptable as a reaction to a situation. Violence isn't an acceptable form of anger.

☺ To be socially aware – empathise with others and their emotions (remember not everyone will feel the same way as you).

☺ To manage our relationships – communicate clearly with others and to be able to manage conflict with others.

Who Can Help?

One Good Adult

Dear Emma,

I've never written to a problem page before but I don't know really what else to do. I am so stressed at the moment, everything seems to be getting on top of me. I can't cope at all. Last week in class I totally lost it with my friend, screamed my head off and stormed out of the classroom. I ended up in detention again adding to my stress. My exams are coming up but I can't study at home as my mum is sick and I care for her and my two younger brothers. My life just seems useless. I started taking drink from home to make the pressure go away but I know deep down this isn't right and I think my mum suspects and she doesn't need the extra stress of me. I feel sick.

Seán

THINK, PAIR, SHARE

Responsible

5. Good Advice

(a) On your own, write down the advice you might give Seán if he asked you for help.

_____

_____

_____

(b) How do you think Seán might react to these options?

_____

_____

_____

(c) With your partner, share what you've written and decide what might be the best option for Seán.

_____

_____

_____

Link Up
See also Module 4,
Substance Use, page 89

S. Mental Illness

Just like any area of our body which may become ill during our lifetime, the mind can also become unwell and need some help to recover. If we look after our mental wellbeing as part of our overall health, recovering should be much easier.

Mental illnesses are health conditions involving changes in thinking, emotion or behaviour (or a combination of these). Mental illnesses are associated with distress and/or problems functioning in social, work or family activities. www.psychiatry.org

GROUP ACTIVITY

1. In small groups try to think of words or terms that are often used to describe mental illness. Think of terms used by your family and friends, in the media or generally in our culture. Classify them as derogatory (insulting or offensive) or medical terms.

Derogatory	Medical	Appropriate to Use (Yes/No)

How Is Mental Illness Classified?

There are many different methods of classifying mental illness. The World Health Organisation's classification for mental disorders consists of the following main groups:

- Organic, including symptomatic, mental disorders
- Mental and behavioural disorders due to use of psychoactive substances
- Schizophrenia, schizotypal and delusional disorders
- Mood (affective) disorders
- Neurotic, stress-related and somatoform disorders
- Behavioural syndromes associated with physiological disturbances and physical factors
- Disorders of personality and behaviour in adult persons
- Mental retardation
- Disorders of psychological development
- Behavioural and emotional disorders with onset usually occurring in childhood and adolescence

In addition, there is a group of unspecified mental disorders.

If you look at the list carefully, are you surprised by how many of the terms are familiar to you or that some are included on the list at all?

This list may vary slightly throughout the world but in general these are the most identifiable ones at present. Knowing these classifications will allow you to have a better understanding of the complexities of mental health.

What Is My Attitude to Mental Illness?

TABLE ACTIVITY

2. **Tick the boxes in the table below.** Discuss your answers with the person sitting beside you.

		Agree	Disagree	Unsu
1	**I know someone who has suffered from a mental illness (only answer this question if you feel comfortable doing so).**			
2	**People who have a mental illness should be allowed to work.**			
3	**The media portrays mental illness in a positive way.**			
4	**Mental illness is attention seeking.**			
5	**People who have a mental illness shouldn't be allowed have any contact with children.**			
6	**If my friend confided in me that they had a mental illness I would not want to know them anymore.**			
7	**Mental illness can be cured.**			
8	**Everyone has the potential to develop a mental illness.**			
9	**Substance misuse doesn't contribute to mental illness.**			

10	Eating disorders are one of the most common mental conditions in teenagers.				
11	There is a stigma attached to having a mental illness.				
12	Suicide and self-harming are not forms of mental illness.				

THINK, PAIR, SHARE

3. Teenagers and mental illness

(a) Pick two statements from the list above that you think might be relevant to teenagers today. Why do you think they are relevant?

_____

_____

_____

(b) Share what you wrote down with your partner.

TRB

Depression

Depression is a serious medical illness that negatively affects how you feel, the way you think and how you act.

Depression is one of the most common mental illnesses and it affects nearly twice as many women as men. There is no age profile for depression, it can occur at any time. Late teens and mid twenties is often when it occurs as well as in older adults. Some people may experience one episode of depression while other people may have various episodes throughout their life. Depression is very treatable and once a person recognises the symptoms they can receive help.

The World Health Organisation defines depression as 'a common mental disorder, characterized by sadness, loss of interest or pleasure, feelings of guilt or low self-worth, disturbed sleep or appetite, feelings of tiredness and poor concentration'.

Depression - Three Different Types

1. Reactive Depression: This often occurs if a person experiences a loss, e.g. death of a loved one. However some people are more susceptible to this type of depression than others.
2. Unipolar or Endogenous Depression: This is a persistent feeling of sadness, solely focused on the negative emotions experienced.
3. Bipolar Disorder or Manic Depressive Illness: This is a situation where the person alternates between elation and depression.

Did you know that **aetiology** is the study of the causes of a disease or mental disorder?

What are the Symptoms of Depression?

There are a number of different symptoms but the prevailing one is of sadness and a lost interest in life. Other symptoms which are common include:

- Weight loss without dieting or weight gain
- Insomnia or oversleeping
- Loss of energy or increased fatigue
- Restlessness or irritability
- Feelings of worthlessness or inappropriate guilt
- Difficulty thinking, concentrating or making decisions
- Thoughts of death or suicide
- Attempt at suicide

If you know someone who may be experiencing some of the above symptoms or if you are yourself it is very important that you speak to someone who can help and advise you, e.g. a teacher, a guidance counsellor, your parents, your friends, an older brother / sister / cousin.

What's the Difference between Sadness and Depression?

'I felt sad when my granddad died but I didn't think I was depressed. Was I?' Probably not if you were still going about your daily life but felt sad when you thought of your granddad or memories of experiences you shared. This was a normal response to a stressful event in your life. Sadness and depression are not the same. Feelings of sadness will lessen with time.

These websites have information about depression and mental health that you might find useful:

www.yourmentalhealth.ie   www.stateofmindireland.ie
www.mentalhealthireland.ie   www.reachout.com
www.aware.ie   www.pieta.ie

One Good Adult

Don't forget to ask for help!

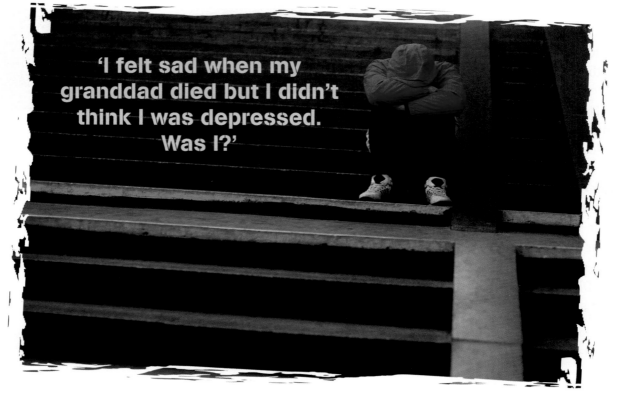

'I felt sad when my granddad died but I didn't think I was depressed. Was I?'

The old saying that time is a great healer does actually have a lot of truth attached. In time the memories of your granddad won't make you sad but you will feel happy to have had this time with him.

What Causes a Person to be Clinically Depressed?

Clinical depression can carry on for months and even years. As depression can affect anyone a number of factors have been identified:

1. Biochemistry

Abnormalities in the balance of some brain chemicals, e.g. serotonin and nonadrenaline, may contribute to some symptoms of depression, e.g. fatigue, irritability.

2. Genetics

Depression can often be found in a number of family members.

3. Personality

If a person has low self-esteem, finds it difficult to manage stressful situations or is generally pessimistic, they could be more vulnerable to depression.

4. Environmental factors

If a person is continuously exposed to abuse, violence, neglect or poverty and may be predisposed to depression, they could suffer from the illness. It is also important to be aware that a medical condition, e.g. brain tumour or vitamin deficiency, can cause depression too.

> **Link Up**
> See also Module 4: Substance Use, Self Esteem, page 112

Treatment

Depression can be treated in a number of ways. For some people a change in diet, more exercise or even taking a holiday can be sufficient treatment. However for others, different forms of intervention may be needed. Depression is treated very successfully and most people respond well to the treatment.

The initial stage of getting treatment is often a visit to your local GP who may refer you to a psychiatrist to conduct a diagnostic evaluation of your situation. This involves an interview and maybe a physical examination. This evaluation may then be able to reveal specific symptoms, build a profile of medical and family history and any contributing environmental factors. Once this is done treatment can be decided.

> **Link Up**
> See also Module 6: Physical Activity and Nutrition, page 171

Two of the most popular and successful ways of treating depression are medication and psychotherapy.

Medication

Antidepressants may be prescribed to correct imbalances in the levels of chemicals in the brain. This medication is not habit forming (addictive) when prescribed and used as directed.

A person may notice an improvement within the first week or so but for some people it can take a couple of months for any changes to be felt. If a person doesn't feel any better after a number of months, the dose prescribed may need to be altered to become more effective. Psychiatrists usually recommend that patients continue to take medication for six months or more after symptoms have improved. However if a person experiences a number of episodes of depression, a more long-term maintenance plan may be suggested.

Psychotherapy

This involves the person talking to a professional counsellor or taking part in a group therapy session. Someone with mild depression may only need to attend for a number of weeks, while for others, a combination of medication and therapy is necessary. In recent years, Cognitive Behavioural Therapy (CBT) has become increasingly popular as a method of treating people who suffer with depression. This type of therapy focuses on the link between thoughts, emotion and behaviour. CBT helps to identify negative thoughts and feelings which are affecting a person's behaviour and changes them to positive thoughts and actions. Over a period of time it is envisaged that the person will replace negative thoughts with positive thoughts.

Regular exercise has also proved to be a successful treatment for depression

REFLECTION

4. Identify why some forms of treatment might be used over others and how do you think this might benefit the person?

_____

_____

_____

_____

_____

_____

Mindfulness

TRB

Mindfulness refers to the awareness that emerges by paying attention, on purpose, non-judgementally to the present moment. (Jon Kabat-Zinn)

Mindfulness is about being fully present in the moment. Many people practise mindfulness to cope with the everyday stresses of life, but some people also use mindfulness to help them with their depression. Mindfulness is not relaxation, nor is it a religion, though some religions, such as Buddhism, use it. While mindfulness has been in existence for centuries, it has only recently emerged within the general population as a coping strategy. In the late 1970s Jon Kabat-Zinn developed a programme to teach mindfulness to people who had chronic illness and pain. A group of psychologists then developed this further to create Mindfulness Based Cognitive Therapy (MBCT) to prevent the recurrence of depression.

Ellie Goulding

'I was sceptical [about having cognitive behavioural therapy] at first because I'd never had therapy, but not being able to leave the house [because of panic attacks] was so debilitating. And this was when my career was really taking off ... My surroundings would trigger a panic attack, so I couldn't go to the studio unless I was lying down in the car with a pillow over my face. I used to beat myself up about it. There were a couple of times after I released *Delirium* when I was doing promo and thought, "Oh god, it's coming back, it's coming back," but it didn't. I think my body has become quite good at controlling anxiety.'

Read more at www.marieclaire.co.uk — search for: celebrities speak mental health.

Four ways to add mindfulness to your day

Remember: consistency is key.

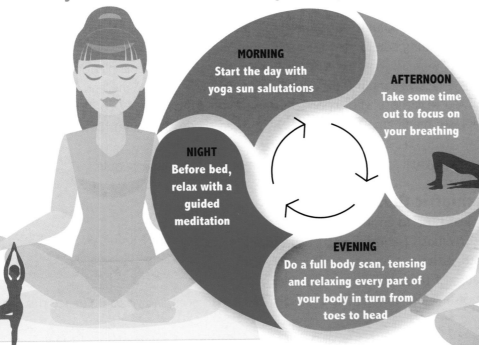

MORNING
Start the day with yoga sun salutations

AFTERNOON
Take some time out to focus on your breathing

NIGHT
Before bed, relax with a guided meditation

EVENING
Do a full body scan, tensing and relaxing every part of your body in turn from toes to head

Spend just 10–15 minutes on each activity every day to feel the benefits of mindfulness in your life.

Link Up
See also Module 5: Relationships and Sexuality Education.

Post-Partum Depression (Post-Natal Depression)

For many women giving birth is a wonderful experience. However some women may feel depressed. It is thought that up to 70% of all women suffer from 'baby blues' which is a short-term condition involving sadness, irritability, anxiety and restlessness. Post-partum depression (PPD) can last for several months.

Symptoms of post-partum depression include:

- Sluggishness, fatigue
- Feeling sad, hopeless, helpless or worthless
- Difficulty sleeping / sleeping too much
- Changes in appetite
- Difficulty concentrating / confusion
- Crying for no reason
- Lack of interest in the baby
- Fear of harming the baby or oneself

It is important that women receive help if they are suffering from PPD, as sometimes they can feel isolated, ashamed or guilty about how they are feeling when magazines, media and other new mothers are full of stories of great joy.

GROUP ACTIVITY

5. Do you think that the media are irresponsible in publishing stories about celebrity pregnancies and their need to return to pre-pregnancy shape very soon after giving birth? Is this a realistic expectation of new mothers? Discuss as a group

Link Up
See also Module 1:
Self-Management, Digital Wellbeing, page 17.

Social Media and Depression

A recent study has found that the use of multiple social media platforms is more strongly associated with depression and anxiety among young adults than time spent online. `TRB`

In a US survey, 1,787 young adults were asked about their use of 11 popular social media platforms: Facebook, YouTube, Twitter, Google Plus, Instagram, Snapchat, Reddit, Tumblr, Pinterest, Vine, and LinkedIn. Analysis of the survey data showed that those who reported using the most platforms (7 to 11) had more than three times the risk of depression and anxiety than those who used the least amount (0 to 2). (Source: psychnews.psychiatryonline.org)

While social media platforms are a virtual space, they create real emotions for young people.

Marijuana Use and Psychiatric Disorders

Several studies have linked marijuana use to an increased risk of psychiatric disorders, including psychosis (schizophrenia), depression, anxiety and substance use disorders. It's not easy to measure to what extent marijuana is the main cause of these conditions. However, the amount of it used, the age of first use and genetic vulnerability have all been shown to influence this relationship.

Link Up
See also Module 4:
Substance Use, page 89.

According to a 2017 report by the American National Academies of Sciences, Engineering and Medicine, health care professionals need more evidence to make sound decisions about marijuana and other cannabinoids, which act in a similar way.

Among the report's conclusions were:

✎ There is strong evidence that marijuana use increases the risk of developing schizophrenia and other causes of psychosis, with the highest risk amongst frequent users

✎ Some evidence suggests a small increased risk of developing depressive disorders

All psychoactive drugs, including cannabis, can seriously affect the growing teenage brain, most notably in the Nucleus Accumbens, an important connection in the set of neural pathways commonly called the 'reward circuit'. The pleasurable feeling you get when you see or experience something that makes you happy is because of activation in this important brain area. Because of this 'feel good' reaction, the Nucleus Accumbens is also a big factor in the development of addictions.

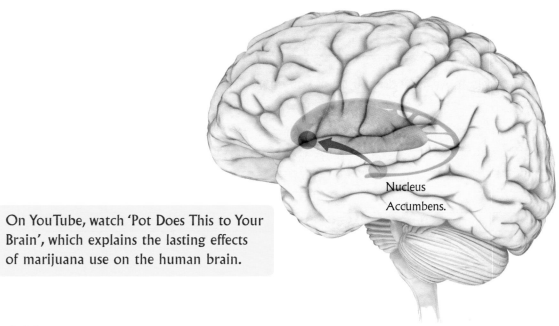

Nucleus Accumbens.

On YouTube, watch 'Pot Does This to Your Brain', which explains the lasting effects of marijuana use on the human brain.

Suicide

The more severe forms of depression carry a suicidal risk as the patient sees little hope for the future and is preoccupied with negative thoughts about his or her abilities. Left untreated such depressions can result in suicide. Some 15% of those with a depressive illness take their own lives. Suicidal thoughts as opposed to actions are very common.

Connecting for Life is the national strategy to reduce suicide over the period 2015–2020. It sets out the Irish Government's vision for suicide prevention, the expected outcomes over these five years and the actions that will be taken to prevent suicide and self-harm in Ireland. The strategy has seven goals.

1. Improved understanding: to improve the nation's understanding of and attitudes to suicidal behaviour, mental health and wellbeing

2. Empowered communities: to support local communities' capacity to prevent and respond to suicidal behaviour.

3. Focus on priority groups: to target approaches to reduce suicidal behaviour and improve mental health among priority groups
4. Better access to support: to enhance accessibility, consistency and care pathways of services for people vulnerable to suicidal behaviour
5. High quality services: to ensure safe and high quality services for people vulnerable to suicide
6. Reduced access to means: to reduce and restrict access to means of suicidal behaviour
7. Better data and research: to improve surveillance, evaluation and high quality research relating to suicidal behaviour

Read more at www.hse.ie. Search for: Connecting for Life

WRITTEN ACTIVITY

6. Having read the goals above, how do you think you could help to implement some of them in your school?

_____

_____

_____

_____

_____

Self-Harm

The infographic below describes the rates of self-harm in Ireland in 2016.

2016 statistics at a glance

Presentations **11,485**

Persons **8,909**

2007   2016   **+10%**

Rate in 2016 10% higher than 2007

RATES

206

per 100,000

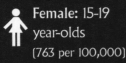 **Male:** 20-24 years old
(516 per 100,000)
1 in every 194

1 in every 485

had a self-harm act

Female: 15-19 year-olds
(763 per 100,000)

Peak rates were among young people

Method

2 in every 3

involved **overdose**

 67%

1 in every 3

involved **alcohol**

34%   **29%**

Men   Women

One-quarter

involved **self-cutting**

 27%

TIME

Peak Time

Midnight

3am

7pm

Almost **half** of presentations were made between 7pm -3am

M T W T F S S

Monday, Tuesday and **Sunday** had the highest number of self-harm presentations

---

Treatment

 71% received an assessment in the ED

 76% received a follow-up recommendation after discharge

 13% left the ED without being seen

Urban   Rural

Higher incidence of self-harm in urban areas

Source: E. Griffin, C.B. Dillon, E. Arensman, P. Corcoran, E Williamson, IJ Perry (2017). National Self-Harm Registry Ireland Annual Report 2016. Cork: National Suicide Research Foundation.

7. From the following list of mental illnesses pick one and research it. Then give a final presentation to your class group. This also may be a suitable opportunity to have a mental health day in your school. Maybe create a leaflet or update the school website, make a presentation to the rest of the school about the different ways in which mental illness can affect people.

Topics

- Bipolar Disorder
- Obsessive Compulsive Disorder
- Schizophrenia
- Substance Use and Depression
- Social Media and Depression
- Obesity
- Eating Disorders
- Impact of Social Media on Our Wellbeing

REMEMBER:

If we look at the statistics most people will be aware of someone who has had a depressive episode in their life.

Colour and Emotion

The mood-altering effects of colour have been used for centuries. The ancient Chinese and Egyptians used the idea of colour therapy or chromotherapy to heal. Even today in holistic therapy, chromotherapy is practised, although research suggests that a person's mood in a room is only affected by colour for a short period of time. Our emotions are very closely linked to colour, e.g 'he saw red', 'I'm feeling blue'.

Chromotherapy

Red was used to stimulate the body and mind and to increase circulation. **Yellow** was thought to stimulate the nerves and to purify the body. **Orange** was used to heal the lungs and to increase energy levels.
Blue was believed to soothe illnesses and treat pain. **Indigo** was thought to alleviate skin problems.

Cultural variation in the impact of colour

White is the colour of death in China but purple represents death in Brazil. Yellow is sacred in Chinese culture but represents sadness in Greece and jealousy in France. In North America green signifies jealousy, e.g. green with envy, the green-eyed monster.

Red: Urgency, passion, heat, love, blood, excitement, strength, sex, speed, danger

Yellow: Warmth, sunshine, cheer, happiness, cowardice, brightness

Blue: Truth, dignity, power, coolness, melancholy, heaviness, trust, reliability, belonging

Orange: Playfulness, warmth, vibrancy

Green: Nature, health, cheerfulness, environment, money, vegetation, fresh, cool, growth, abundance

Purple: Wealth, royalty, sophistication, intelligence, spirituality, dignity

Pink: Soft, sweet, nurture, security

Black: Sophistication, elegant, seductive, mystery, death, rebellion, strength, evil

White: Purity, cleanliness, lightness, emptiness, virginal, youthful, mild

Gold: Prestige, expensive

Silver: Prestige, cold, scientific

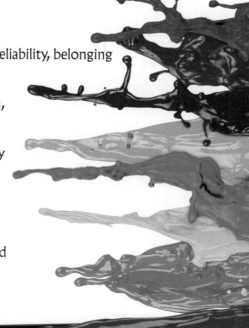

Other Mediums and How They Express Mental Health

Throughout history, mental health has been written about in songs, poetry, drama etc. Can you name any songs or films or have you studied any plays where mental health issues were a theme?

Some examples are given below:

Films:

- *A Beautiful Mind*
- *Girl, Interrupted*
- *Donnie Darko*
- *As Good as it Gets*

- *World's Greatest Dad*
- *Inside Out*
- *Cake*
- *Sylvia*

- *The Hours*
- *Little Miss Sunshine*
- *It's Kind of a Funny Story*

Songs:

- 'I Don't Like Mondays' – The Boomtown Rats
- 'Paint it Black' – The Rolling Stones

- 'The Fear' – Lily Allen
- 'Lithium' – Nirvana
- 'Fight Song' – Rachel Platten
- 'Warrior' – Demi Lovato

- 'Shake It Out' – Florence and the Machine
- 'The Monster' – Eminem (feat. Rihanna)

6. Building Health Literacy

Having looked at some of the challenges and ways to overcome mental health issues, it's important to remember to tell someone if you are feeling sad or stressed about an issue: it always helps to share how you are feeling with another person.

It is important to know where to go for advice and help if you or a friend ever needs it. The following are a list of organisations/websites that provide advice.

ORGANISATION NAME	WEBSITE DETAILS	FUNCTION OF ORGANISATION
Mental Health Ireland	www.mentalhealthireland.ie	Promotes positive mental health and actively supports people with a mental illness, their families and carers by identifying their needs and advocating their rights.
Aware	www.aware.ie	Helping to defeat depression.
Department of Health and Children	www.dohc.ie	Provides information about the government health services available in Ireland.
Health Service Executive	www.hse.ie	Provides links to sites for the Irish Health Boards.
Reach Out!	www.reachout.com.au	A site that helps young people through tough times.
Youth	www.youth.ie	A site that focuses on all things youthful in Ireland today.
Youth Health	www.youthhealthinfo.com	Information for young people.
Spunout	www.spunout.ie	Forum for young people to discuss various issues from work to school to alcohol abuse.
Your Mental Health	www.yourmentalhealth.ie	An information resource for people in crisis.
Irish Association of Suicidology	www.ias.ie	Individuals and groups sharing knowledge about suicide.

7. Your Life Plan: How Has It Changed?

PERSONALITY TYPE

1. Circle your personality type below. You identified this already in the Life Plan at the beginning of the book.

2. Your personality can directly impact how you understand, accept or reject some of the concepts in this module. What changes or challenges are ahead of you?

   _____
   _____
   _____

3. How might you learn to deal with these changes or challenges? Think of your multiple intelligences. These may offer clues as to how you may best approach these changes or challenges.

   _____
   _____
   _____

REALITY CHECK

4. Thinking about what we've explored in this module, fill out your Wheel of Life again.

(a)   Has anything changed?   Y ☐   N ☐
(b)   If so, what has changed and why?

   _____
   _____
   _____

(c)   Do you need to take action in any area?   Y ☐   N ☐
(d)   If so, what actions do you need to take?

   _____
   _____
   _____

(e)   Identify who might help you achieve these actions.

   _____

GOALS

Do you need to set a goal for this area in your life? If so, go to page 223 for a Goal Worksheet.

Module 3: Gender Studies

If I Were A Boy

Songwriters:
Carlson, Britney; Gad, Toby;
Knowles, Beyonce;

If I were a boy even just for a day,
I'd roll out of bed in the morning,
And throw on what I wanted,
And go drink beer with the guys,
And chase after girls,
I'd kick it with who I wanted,
And I'd never get confronted for it,
'Cause they stick up for me,
If I were a boy, I think I could understand
How it feels to love a girl, I swear I'd be a better man
I'd listen to her,
'Cause I know how it hurts,
When you lose the one you wanted,
'Cause he's taking you for granted,
And everything you had got destroyed.

If I were a boy, I would turn off my phone,
Tell everyone it's broken,
So they'd think that I was sleeping alone,
I'd put myself first,
And make the rules as I go,
'Cause I know that she'd be faithful,
Waiting for me to come home, to come home,

It's a little too late for you to come back,
Say it's just a mistake,
Think I'd forgive you like that,
If you thought I would wait for you,
You thought wrong.
But you're just a boy,
You don't understand,
And you don't understand,
Oh how it feels to love a girl,
Someday you wish you were a better man,
You don't listen to her,
You don't care how it hurts,
Until you lose the one you wanted,
'Cause you're taking her for granted,
And everything you had got destroyed,
But you're just a boy.

DISCUSS

Read through the lyrics. Discuss the characteristics of boys and girls (men and women) in this song.
Do you think that the lyrics describe the true nature of men and women? Give reasons for your answer.

Introduction

This module may challenge your understanding of what it means to be a man or woman in society. It allows you to explore what shapes our understanding of masculinity and femininity and how that varies across cultures, races and classes. Most importantly, it examines how such views of men and women influence our health and wellbeing.

1. Understanding Gender

See also Module 5, Sexual Identity page 152

Gender Versus Sex

The differences between these two ideas can be linked to the Nature Versus Nurture debate.

Nurture is the effect the people in your life have on you growing up, e.g. the values your parents taught you. **Nature** is the genetics you receive, e.g. eye colour.

What do we mean by sex and gender?

Sometimes it is hard to understand exactly what is meant by the term **gender** and how it differs from the closely related term **sex**.

Sex refers to the biological and physiological characteristics that define men and women.

Gender refers to the socially constructed roles, behaviours, activities and attributes that a given society considers appropriate for men and women.

To put it another way:

- Male and female are sex categories, while masculine and feminine are gender categories.
- Aspects of sex will not vary substantially between different human societies, while aspects of gender may vary greatly.

Some examples of sex characteristics:

- Women menstruate while men do not.
- Men have testicles while women do not.
- Women have developed breasts that are usually capable of lactating, while men have not.
- Men generally have denser bones than women.

Some examples of gender characteristics:

- In the United States (and most other countries), women earn significantly less money than men for similar work.
- In Vietnam, more men than women smoke, as smoking is not traditionally considered appropriate behaviour by women.
- In most of the world, women do more housework than men.

Source: World Health Organisation (WHO), 2010

ACTIVITY

1. **Think back to your first awareness that you were different from members of the opposite sex.** This could be a memory of a time when you were treated or expected to behave differently from others of the opposite sex.

In your copybook, answer the following questions.
(a) What were the circumstances?
(b) When did this occur?
(c) Who was involved?
(d) Where were you when this happened?
(e) How did you feel?
(f) Where did your ideas about gender come from?

1. **Gender** refers to the socially constructed characteristics of women and men — such as the norms, roles and relationships that exist between them. Gender expectations vary between cultures and can change over time. It is also important to recognise identities that do not fit into the binary male or female sex categories. Gender norms, relations and roles also impact the health outcomes of people with transgender or intersex identities.

2. While most people are born either male or female (biological sex), they are taught appropriate behaviours for males and females (gender norms) — including how they should interact with others of the same or opposite sex within households, communities and workplaces (gender relations) and which functions or responsibilities they should assume in society (gender roles).
    (**Source:** World Health Organisation, 2015, Gender, Fact Sheet 403)

3. **There are two gender roles:** Masculine refers to qualities or characteristics associated with being a boy or a man. Feminine refers to qualities or characteristics associated with being a girl or a woman.

4. **Androgyny** is a combination or balance of masculinity and femininity. It allows for the possibility that individuals can express both masculinity and femininity.

5. **Gender Identity:** This is often referred to as femininity and masculinity and refers to the degree to which persons see themselves as masculine or feminine given what it means to be a man or woman in society. Society decides what being male or female means.

2. What traits do you think are associated with being:

(a) Feminine: _____

_____

(b) Masculine: _____

_____

EQUALITY   **EQUITY**

(**Source:** Interaction Institute for Social Change. Artist: Angus Maguire.)

6.   **Gender equity:** The Interaction Institute developed the iconic image above of three individuals [TRB] of different heights who are trying to watch a baseball game over a fence. If we were to treat them **equally,** we would simply give each the same sized box to stand on. However, this does not have the same impact on each, as the shortest person still cannot see. In order to give **equitable** treatment, each person would need to be given a different sized box to stand on that would enable each to have a clear view over the fence. Note the tallest does not require a box in this case.

2. Social Construction of Gender

1. Examine the diagram of the Genderbread Person v3.3 and answer the following questions.

The Genderbread Person v3.3

by it's pronounced METROsexual .com

Gender is one of those things everyone thinks they understand, but most people don't. Like *Inception*. Gender isn't binary. It's not either/or. In many cases it's both/and. A bit of this, a dash of that. This tasty little guide is meant to be an appetizer for gender understanding. It's okay if you're hungry for more. In fact, that's the idea.

Plot a point on both continua in each category to represent your identity; combine all ingredients to form your Genderbread

4 (of infinite) possible plot and label combos

Identity

Attraction

Expression

Sex

Ø Indicates a lack of what's on the right.

Gender Identity
Woman-ness
Man-ness

How you, in your head, define your gender, based on how much you align (or don't align) with what you understand to be the options for gender.

"woman" "man"
"two-spirit" "genderqueer"

Gender Expression
Feminine
Masculine

The ways you present gender, through your actions, dress, and demeanor, and how those presentations are interpreted based on gender norms.

"butch" "femme"
"androgynous" "gender neutral"

Biological Sex
Female-ness
Male-ness

The physical sex characteristics you're born with and develop, including genitalia, body shape, voice pitch, body hair, hormones, chromosomes, etc.

"male" "female"
"intersex" "MtF Female"

Sexually Attracted to
Nobody {
(Women/Females/Femininity)
(Men/Males/Masculinity)

Romantically Attracted to
Nobody {
(Women/Females/Femininity)
(Men/Males/Masculinity)

In each grouping, circle all that apply to you and plot a point, depicting the aspects of gender toward which you experience attraction.

For a bigger bite, read more at http://bit.ly/genderbread

(a) What do you think is the difference between gender identity and gender expression?

_____

_____

_____

(b) How do people generally express their gender?

_____

_____

_____

(c) How effective is the Genderbread Person image in explaining the complexities of gender and sex?

_____

_____

_____

More and more, people are being asked to state which gender they most identify with, e.g. when filling out personal details on forms.

Dr James Barry

Margaret Bulkley was born in Cork in 1789 into a respectable family. When her father lost his business, the family was thrown into poverty. She fled to London with her mother and was taken in by her uncle, the famous painter James Barry. While there, Margaret hatched a remarkable plan: she would become a surgeon. In those days, women were not allowed to study medicine, so she decided to disguise herself as a man. She adopted her uncle's name and enrolled at Edinburgh University. Though the work was gruelling she did well and, on qualifying, became a surgeon in the British army, travelling and working all over the British Empire.

Over her long career, she was well-respected and in demand as a private doctor with the wealthy and the nobility. She was a pioneer in hospital hygiene and of new techniques — in 1826 she carried out the first ever successful caesarean section where both mother and baby survived. And while people often thought the doctor strange, no one suspected she was a woman — if they had, they would never have believed it. In those days, it was thought that no woman would be able for the physical or intellectual challenges of surgery. But Margaret fooled them all and excelled at every aspect of her difficult career. She also became notorious for her temper and intolerance — no doubt due to the stress of maintaining her deception for such a long time.

She died in 1865, leaving instructions that her body not be examined and she be buried in the clothes she was wearing. However the woman who laid out the body discovered her secret and made the news public. It was a huge scandal at the time but her story has, sadly, largely been forgotten.

DISCUSS

2. Having read about Dr James Barry, discuss the following with your partner or in small groups.
   (a) What do you think are the differences between life for women and for men in the 19th century and the present day?
   (b) What are the key changes in the rights of women from the 19th to the 21st century?
   (c) What do you think must happen next to ensure equity for all genders?

Gender and Cultural Differences

RESEARCH

3. Differences in clothing for men and women
   (a) What is the purpose of the burqa in the Islamic tradition?
   (b) Do men have to observe the same rules?
   (c) What is a burkini?
   (d) Are there other religious groups that instruct women to follow a particular dress code? Why is this?

RESEARCH

4. In small groups, for each image:

(a) Identify the religion depicted.

(b) Describe how men and women are viewed in each religion.

3. Understanding Difference

Being heterosexual/straight

People often think that being heterosexual is easy. Whatever your developing sexuality, it can be scary and frightening. The thought of asking somebody out may make you feel nervous or embarrassed, or you may feel that you should be attracted to people and want sex when actually you don't. Many people feel like this. You are not alone! There are people you can talk to about relationships. If you feel that you cannot talk to someone you know, you could try contacting a helpline.

Being homosexual/gay or lesbian

It is estimated that approximately 10% of people are gay. Gay is a general term that refers to someone who is attracted to another person of the same sex. Homosexual men can be referred to as gay and homosexual women can be referred to as lesbian, although the word gay can be used to refer to both men and women.

Being bisexual or transgendered

It is not unusual for some people to be attracted to people of both genders. This is referred to as being bisexual. However, just because you might have an attraction to someone of the same sex, it doesn't necessarily mean you are bisexual. It is quite common for people to experiment and fantasise at some stage. Transgendered is a term that refers to people who find themselves feeling like they are in the wrong body, i.e. a man who feels more like a woman.

Being lesbian, gay, bisexual or transgendered

Some people are prejudiced against gay and lesbian people. This is wrong. Whatever you think you are, it's ok. The world tends to think that everyone will be heterosexual; therefore if you think you might be gay, lesbian, bisexual or transgendered, it can feel very lonely and isolating. Some people say they 'felt like they were the only one'. But you are not alone. Although we don't know the exact figures, it is estimated that in every 100 people, 10 will be gay or lesbian.

Try and find somebody you can talk to about it. This might be a friend, a student counsellor or a trusted adult. You can also phone a helpline.

Some points to keep in mind:

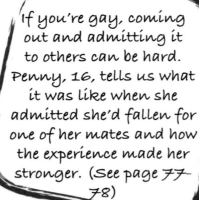

If you're gay, coming out and admitting it to others can be hard. Penny, 16, tells us what it was like when she admitted she'd fallen for one of her mates and how the experience made her stronger. (See page 77-78)

It is quite natural to be confused about your sexuality when growing up, so take your time to figure it out.

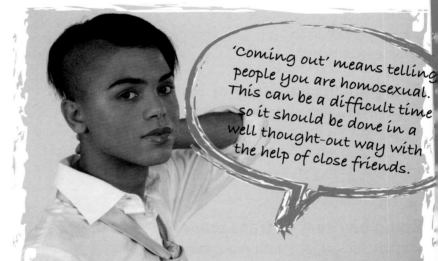

'Coming out' means telling people you are homosexual. This can be a difficult time so it should be done in a well thought-out way with the help of close friends.

Everyone is different. Some people think that not being heterosexual is somehow wrong, and they bully and discriminate against these people. This is wrong and should not happen. Whoever you are, you have a human right to be you!

Friends, peers and society can pressure us into being someone we are not. This is wrong. Everyone has the right to be who they want to be without fear of discrimination, bullying or prejudice.

Sadly, many gay people face a difficult time being accepted by friends, family or the community. This can be a lonely and frustrating time but you needn't be alone. There are more gay people than you think, and many organisations offer support, guidance, and advice for gay people and their families.

Diary Entry

Penny's Story

20 December

I can't truly pinpoint the exact day or hour when it started, when I began to like Sara. I go to an all-girls school, and my social life is fairly limited, I didn't know any boys at all but had quite a few good friends in the school.

We were friends, made each other laugh and each time I'd catch a glimpse of her green eyes, defined by the black eyeliner, my stomach would jolt. Of course I never truly realised this until some time later.

27 December

Over the Christmas holidays, I kept thinking of her. I kept disregarding it as a phase or something that was just my way of getting attention, but eventually the thoughts got more and more persistent.

7 January

Eventually, I decided to tell her. I came back, and we were in a history lesson. We were passing notes and she asked why I was crying. I told her I was in love with someone I shouldn't be. She asked if it was a girl, to which I replied 'yes'. She reassured me, told me there were lots of girls 'like me' and that it was fine as long as I didn't act upon it.

When the lesson finished she hugged me and asked me who it was and I told her it was her. Things went downhill very fast. I was cast out of her social group, she refused to look at me and soon the whole school knew.

9 January

I made different attempts to reach Sara, to tell her that it didn't mean anything, that I'm still the same person, that I would do nothing like kiss her and I only thought she deserved to know. I cried all the time, but she pushed me further and further away.

20 June

In the summer holidays, I tried to make my peace. I approached her, trembling, and she wouldn't listen; she kept talking to other people and not seeing me. I left it.

4 September

I came back to school and soon began to isolate myself again and go eat lunch in the toilets. The rumours had stopped, but the after-effects were still there and it still hurt.

At this stage now, I am still unsure about my sexuality. If someone asks if I'm a lesbian I reply 'no', which isn't truly lying because I'm bisexual or just simply curious and open-minded.

10 October

I don't regret having confessed, at all, even after all the bad stuff that happened. What I did was what I considered to be right, and I am proud of that. It showed me who my friends truly are and it showed me how shallow and narrow-minded people can be.

If you are unsure about what you want to do, I say do what's in your heart, and it will be the right choice. You want people to accept you for who you are, not who they expect or want you to be. And if they can't do that, then they are not worth it.

If you are alone, and you can still manage, they are scared of you. They can't see how someone can survive on their own, but I made it, and now I stick up for what I believe is right.

I have written speeches about homophobia in schools, which just totally shut them up.

Have courage. It will work out in the end. You will feel the satisfaction of being true to yourself and that is the most special thing in the world. Nobody can take that away from you.

In our hearts and in our laws, we must treat our people with fairness and dignity, regardless of their race, religion, gender or sexual orientation.
Bill Clinton, 42nd President of America

We want to make sure that prosperity is spread across the spectrum of regions and occupations and genders and races.
Barack Obama, 44th President of America

Coming Out

Coming out is a highly individual process. Why do you think this is the case?

_____

_____

_____

_____

4. Stereotyping

Gender Straitjackets

A recent study has found that, all over the world, young boys are generally encouraged to go outside, exploring and playing freely, while girls are encouraged to stay home and do chores. Over four years, researchers for the Global Early Adolescent Study spoke to 450 children aged 10 to 14 from Bolivia, Belgium, Burkina Faso, China, the Democratic Republic of Congo, Ecuador, Egypt, India, Kenya, Malawi, Nigeria, Scotland, South Africa, the United States and Vietnam.

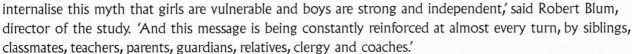

'We found children at a very early age — from the most conservative to the most liberal societies — quickly internalise this myth that girls are vulnerable and boys are strong and independent,' said Robert Blum, director of the study. 'And this message is being constantly reinforced at almost every turn, by siblings, classmates, teachers, parents, guardians, relatives, clergy and coaches.'

The researchers found that these gender-based 'straitjackets' can have really negative effects. Boys can feel pressured to engage in risky behaviours such as taking drugs or smoking. They're also more likely to engage in or be the victims of physical violence. For girls, the attitudes meant to protect them can actually make them more vulnerable, leading them to believe they should give in to the demands of others rather than making their own choices. This can leave girls at greater risk of dropping out of school or suffering sexual violence, child marriage, early pregnancy and so on. In most cultures, girls are discouraged from taking the initiative in any relationship. By 10 years of age they believe that their primary asset is their physical appearance and that they need to look appealing.

Because they've found that these gender roles are so well-established in children by age 10, the researchers believe interventions to change gender stereotyping need to happen far earlier.

TRB

1. Gender stereotypes

   (a) With a partner or in small groups, discuss what you think contributes to 'gender straitjackets' for both girls and boys.

   (b) List three ways that you think we can avoid these gender straitjackets?

   (i) _____

   (ii) _____

   (iii) _____

Challenging Stereotypes (A)
Women During World War II

Before World War II, women were expected to be housewives or to do certain jobs, such as being a nurse, domestic servant or shop assistant. The war changed the world of work for women forever. When men went to fight, women were called upon to fill their jobs, and this included many jobs that were previously thought of as unsuitable for women. Women were called up for war work from March 1941 until May 1945 and worked as the following: mechanics, engineers, tank drivers, ship-builders, factory workers making bombs and aircraft parts, air raid wardens, fire engine drivers, plumbers, ambulance drivers, WRVS (Womens Royal Voluntary Service) and nurses.

Women were required by the government to work. At first, only single women aged 20 to 30 were called up, but by mid 1943, almost 90 per cent of single women and 80 per cent of married women were working in factories, on the land or in the armed forces.

Huge numbers of women were involved in the war effort and many joined the armed forces even though they did not have to. Historical records reveal that there were 640,000 women in the armed forces. Of that number, 55,000 women served with guns and provided essential air defence and 80,000 women were in the Land Army.

Many more women flew unarmed aircraft, drove ambulances, worked as nurses and organised missions from behind enemy lines in the European resistance.

WRITTEN ACTIVITY

3. **Women in the war**

(a) Why did society choose to ignore previous versions of masculinity and femininity during World War II?

_____

_____

(b) What do you think happened in the post-war era when men returned from war?

_____

_____

(c) How did the view of masculinity and femininity change?

_____

_____

Challenging Stereotypes (B)

Anthropologist Margaret Mead addressed the issue of differences in temperament for males and females in *Sex and Temperament in Three Primitive Societies* (1935). This early study led to the conclusion that there are not necessarily differences in traits or temperaments between the sexes. Observed differences in temperament between men and women were not a function of their biological differences. Rather, they resulted from differences in socialisation and the cultural expectations held for each sex. The three societies studied by Mead showed patterns of temperament which were quite varied compared with our own. Among the Arapesh, both males and females displayed what we would consider a 'feminine' temperament (passive, cooperative and expressive). Among the Mundugumor, both males and females displayed what we would consider a 'masculine' temperament (active, competitive and instrumental). Finally, among the Tchambuli, men and women displayed temperaments that were different from each other, but opposite to our own pattern. In that society, men were emotional, and expressive while women were active and instrumental.

Mead's study caused people to rethink the nature of femininity / masculinity. Different gender-related traits, temperaments, roles and identities could no longer be inextricably tied to biological sex.

Source: *What Women Want–What Men Want: Why the Sexes Still See Love and Commitment So Differently* by John Marshall Townsend; Oxford University Press, 1998

WRITTEN ACTIVITY

4. Read the extract and answer the following questions:

(a) How did this article make you feel?

_____

_____

(b) In your opinion, which of the three societies mentioned is best? Why?

_____

_____

Challenging Stereotypes (C)

Matriarchal Societies in the World

In the Xiaolianghshan Mountains, Yunnan province (South East China), live the Mosuo people, one of the last living matriarchal societies today. They are closely related to Tibetans. In their social system, paternity and marriage are not the same as in our world. The main pillar of the family is the mother. The family units can join three female generations with their sons. Grandmothers, mothers and daughters can inhabit the same house without the presence of fathers or husbands. Married couples have what is called a 'walking marriage' or a 'visiting marriage'. This means that the husband visits his wife but always returns afterward to his mother's house. Only uncles, brothers, sons and nephews are happily accepted.

RESEARCH

TRB

5. **Compare and contrast matriarchal societies and patriarchal societies under the following headings:**

   (a) The role of men and women

   _____
   _____
   _____
   _____
   _____
   _____
   _____
   _____
   _____
   _____
   _____
   _____

   (b) Inheritance of property

   _____
   _____
   _____
   _____
   _____
   _____
   _____
   _____
   _____
   _____
   _____

Challenging Stereotypes (D)

Body image expert, Sarah Grogan (1999) describes how society depicts modern woman as Superwoman. She says that this is a myth: 'The myth of Superwoman — baby on the hip, briefcase in one hand, and exercise schedule, credit cards, and flash cards offering quick routes to designer lives clutched in the other.' Sociologists Gilbert & Gilbert contend that 'while the modern man has been exploring his feminine side these femocrats and career women with their suits and briefcases have become the men of our generation . . . moving into positions of power and influence, while the men have become women, learning to bake, wash and care for the kids.'

WRITTEN ACTIVITY

6. Society Today

(a) How true are the observations made about men and women in today's society? Give rea sons for your answer.

_____

_____

(b) Do you think Grogan's and Gilbert & Gilbert's interpretations of how society depicts today's men and women are accurate?

_____

_____

(c) Comment on the idea of the 'femocrat'.

_____

_____

(d) Compare and contrast the idea of the career woman and the career man.

_____

_____

_____

_____

DEBATE

7. As a class debate both of the following topics:
    (a) Feminism has done away with the natural instincts of women.
    (b) Men are expendable.

S. Gender and Sport

Masculinity and the Body

The idea of a link between masculinity and body is often reinforced during schooling through the medium of sport and physical education. Sport is now linked with masculinity as a way of showing physical ability.

To be manly in sports traditionally means to be competitive, successful, dominating, aggressive, stoical, goal-directed and physically strong.

If a man does not possess this muscular shape, he is not deemed masculine by society.

Femininity and Sport

Women have always participated in a great range of sports. Unfortunately, this has not always been recognised by the media and society.

Both physiological and sociological factors have influenced women's participation in sport at all levels. Before the age of 11, boys and girls can compete on equal terms. It is not until after adolescent development that anatomical differences make equal competition between the sexes harder to achieve. These differences are exemplified in bone structure and muscle development.

In terms of performance, the difference between men's and women's records has decreased. Women's performances have radically improved. Also, it is now socially acceptable for women to train and devote a great deal of their life to sport. By having greater access to training facilities and improved training methods, women over the last two decades have been able to attain a higher level of performance.

In the past, women had fewer opportunities in life compared with men. They were expected to run a home and bring up children. In addition to this, it was often seen as unfeminine to participate in sport. As the expectation of women in society changed, so their participation in sport increased.

During World War II women took on jobs previously done by men. After the war many people had a different attitude towards women. This encouraged more women to take part in sport. Women's athletics first appeared in the Olympics programme in 1928. Progress since then has been slow but recently women's events have expanded to include 400-metre hurdles, 1,500-metre middle distance races, 3,000-metre middle distance races and marathons. In the 2008 Beijing Olympics women competed in the pole vault, 3,000-metre steeple chase, 5,000-metre long distance race and the triple jump.

Today a range of sports are open to both male and female participants.

┌───┐

WRITTEN ACTIVITY

Men and women in sport

    (a) Make a list of sports in which men and women compete against each other.

    _____

    _____

    (b) Can you think of any sports that may eventually become mixed competitively?

    _____

    _____

    (c) Are there any sports from which women should be banned from playing? Give reasons for
        your answer.

    _____

    _____

└───┘

Sex Testing in Sport

`TRB`

On 12 August 2016 Dutee Chand became just the second female sprinter to represent India at the Olympic Games. In 2014, the International Association of Athletic Federations banned her from competition on the grounds that her body naturally produced too much testosterone, a condition called hyperandrogenism. It wasn't her fault, the organisation explained. But her condition gave her an unfair edge over other female athletes, according to the IAAF policy. She appealed this decision and it was overturned in time for the Rio Olympics in 2016.

(**Source:** New Republic, 'It's Time to Stop Gender-Testing Athletes')

Here are some details about sex testing, which was introduced more than 40 years ago.

Conducting Tests

Laboratory and genetic testing were introduced at the 1968 Mexico City Olympics. Women typically have two X chromosomes and men have an X and a Y chromosome in each of their cells. The presence of two X chromosomes is taken as confirmation of the athlete's female gender. Test results for about one in 500-600 athletes are abnormal.

Testing

The International Association of Athletics Federations abandoned gender verification tests in the early 1990s, concluding that they were not needed. The International Olympic Committee (IOC) suspended the tests before the 2000 Sydney Olympics. However, the Olympic Council of Asia still conducts tests.

1. Polish sprinter Stanislawa Walasiewicz, who won the women's 100-metre race at the 1932 Los Angeles Olympics, is the most notorious case. She changed her name to Stella Walsh and moved to the United States where she was shot dead in a robbery attempt in 1980. An autopsy showed she possessed male genitalia.

2. The first athlete to fail a sex test was Polish sprinter Eva Klobukowska in 1967, who won a 4 x 100 relay gold medal at the 1964 Tokyo Olympics. She was found to have a rare condition which gave her no advantage over other athletes.

3. Sisters Tamara and Irina Press won five track and field Olympic gold medals for the Soviet Union and set 26 world records in the 1960s. When gender testing was introduced the pair did not compete again.

4. Eight athletes failed the tests at the 1996 Atlanta Olympics but were all cleared by subsequent physical examinations.

5. Britain's Princess Anne, a member of the equestrian team, was excused from the gender test at the 1976

Montreal Olympics.

6. Indian Santhi Soundarajan was stripped of the Asian Games women's 800-metre silver medal after failing a gender test in Doha in 2006. She was admitted to hospital in September 2008 following a suicide bid. She announced in June 2009 that she was turning to coaching.

7. The rapid improvement of South African teenager Caster Semenya (see photo) who won the women's World 800-metre race title in 2009, prompted officials to order a gender verification test.

Caster Semenya

6. Physical Health and Gender

TRB

Moving toward adulthood, men and women tend to have different health behaviours, which are captured in the latest Healthy Ireland Survey. The survey looked at four types of unhealthy behaviours:

- Binge drinking — six or more standard drinks on a single occasion
- Sedentary behaviour — spending eight or more hours sitting in a day
- Smoking
- Eating less than the recommended five portions of fruit and vegetables daily

The survey found that men are much more likely than women to have unhealthy behaviours and to have a higher number of unhealthy behaviours. Men are almost three times more likely than women (14% and 5% respectively) to both smoke and binge drink, and are three times more likely than women (34% and 9% respectively) to both binge drink and not consume the recommended level of fruit and vegetables daily. Almost three times as many men as women exhibit three or more unhealthy behaviours (22% and 8% respectively). All of this means significant health risks to more men than women.

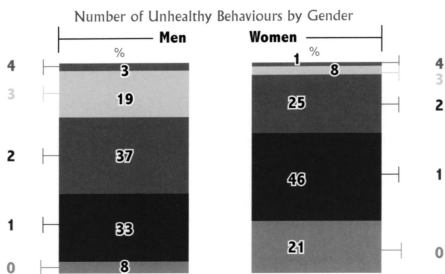

Number of Unhealthy Behaviours by Gender

(**Source:** health.gov.ie, 'Healthy Ireland Survey 2016 — Summary Findings)

DISCUSSION

1. With your partner or in small groups, discuss why you think men and women have different health behaviours?

7. Your Life Plan: How Has It Changed?

1. Circle your personality type below. You identified this already in the Life Plan at the beginning of the book.

2. Your personality can directly impact how you understand, accept or reject some of the concepts in this module. What changes or challenges are ahead of you?

_____

_____

_____

3. How might you learn to deal with these changes or challenges? Think of your multiple intelligences. These may offer clues as to how you may best approach these changes or challenges.

_____

_____

_____

REALITY CHECK

4. Thinking about what we've explored in this module, fill out your Wheel of Life again.

(a) Has anything changed? Y ☐ N ☐

(b) If so, what has changed and why?

_____

_____

(c) Do you need to take action in any area? Y ☐ N ☐

(d) If so, what actions do you need to take?

_____

_____

_____

(e) Identify who might help you achieve these actions.

_____

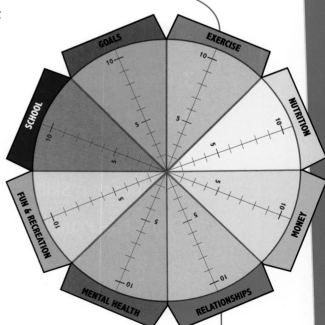

GOALS

5. Do you need to set a goal for this area in your life? If so, go to page 223 for a Goal Worksheet.

Module 4: Substance Use

Introduction

This module offers the opportunity to examine substance use on a variety of levels. Taking psychoactive drugs is a choice. In some cases, such as anaesthetics or prescribed antidepressants, they can help us. But taking non-prescription drugs can get us into trouble with our health, our relationships, our self-worth and our wellbeing. They can have serious consequences for your life and the lives of those around you and lead you down an unhappy and unhealthy path. So spend some time learning the facts, reviewing your personal attitude and considering alternatives in the decision-making process – it might help you to make the right choices.

1. Substance Use

The National Youth Council of Ireland (NYCI) has identified drugs as the most important issue faced by teenagers today. Teenagers know that experimenting with drugs can lead to addiction, a criminal record, serious health risks and loss of life.

So why are teenagers not worried about the consequences of trying drugs? Perhaps because some believe it will never happen to them. Some teenagers have tried smoking cigarettes, cannabis and alcohol and have not become addicted. These people

- may be lucky
- may not have an addictive personality
- may have more emotional outlets and friends to support them
- may have been educated about the risks of drugs and understood the risk of their experimentation
- may just not have liked it

The question is how do you know how it will affect you? Taking the first drug is like playing Russian roulette with a semi-loaded pistol. What will happen when you pull the trigger?

The Department of Health, the Advertising Standards Authority for Ireland (ASAI), family doctors (GPs), the Garda Síochána and many other national organisations have clear guidelines on how to prevent the misuse of nicotine, alcohol and other drugs. However, in the end it is the individual's decision to use a substance or not. The difficulty lies in the consequences of this choice.

'Destiny is no matter of chance. It is a matter of choice. It is not a thing to be waited for; it is a thing to be achieved.' Anonymous

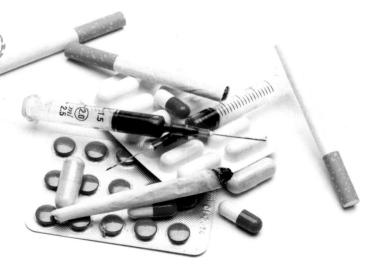

What Is a Drug?

A drug is any substance (apart from food and water) that changes the way the body functions mentally, physically and/or psychologically and/or emotionally. Tobacco, alcohol, cannabis, ecstasy, cocaine and heroin will be discussed in this section as examples of drugs.

It is important to acknowledge that some drugs are used on a regular basis, such as tea and coffee. Both contain caffeine. Some medications can be obtained over the counter in pharmacies. Cigarettes and alcohol, although controlled in their sale, are still accepted in their social use. This can lead to the misconception by some young people that 'everyone else is doing it!' This is not true. Statistics of drug use are getting higher in some cases, but such figures still show that the majority of young people are actually not experimenting with drugs. Drug prevention programmes discourage all young people from trying drugs even once.

Why Do Some Young People Take Drugs?

Young people today are more aware of the new information and communication technologies available to them, e.g. social media, gaming, research and online shopping. Growing up in a strong commercial environment where buying the latest product, brands or fashion is important to fit in adds to the belief that you need 'something' to feel good about yourself or have a good time. Instead of tackling this pressure, some turn to taking a drug that they believe will relieve the stress.

Those teenagers who do not succumb to this temptation are often the ones who have placed more value on themselves, their family, their goals and their interests.

Tobacco, alcohol, cannabis, ecstasy, cocaine and heroin all carry painful stories of personal damage, loss and death. Understanding the facts of each of these drugs is the first step in the decision-making process of how to 'Say No to Drugs'.

2. *Types of Drugs*

Drugs can be categorised in relation to how they affect the body. Different drugs affect different people in different ways. This depends on:

- The type of drug
- The amount used
- Where and how it is used
- The personality of the person using it

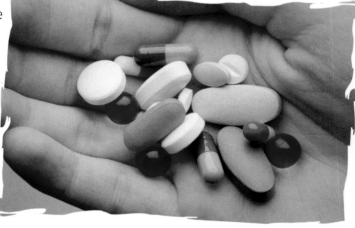

The main types of drugs include:

1. Depressants: Can cause a person to feel more relaxed and less inhibited. In large amounts, they may cause unconsciousness, vomiting and death. Alcohol is a depressant.

2. Minor Tranquillizers: Often prescribed to calm people down or to help them sleep at night. They have the same general effects as depressants. These include benzodiazepines. Valium is an example of a tranquillizer.

3. Opiates: Also known as narcotic analgesics (a type of painkiller that stops pain signals being sent to the brain), these are strong painkillers that produce feelings of happiness (euphoria) and sleepiness. Morphine and heroin are opiates.

4. Stimulants: These are drugs that make people feel more awake, alert and energetic. Cocaine, amphetamines, nicotine and caffeine are stimulants.

5. Hallucinogens: These are drugs that produce strange and intense distortions of perception called

hallucinations. These drugs include LSD (acid) and magic mushrooms.

Many drugs don't belong to just one type. For example, cannabis can act like a depressant as well as causing feelings of happiness. Ecstasy can act as a stimulant and a hallucinogen.

Drugs and the Brain

To understand what happens once a drug has entered the body and made its way to the brain, we first need to understand how the brain absorbs the drug. Look at the diagram below.

Brain's Reward Centre

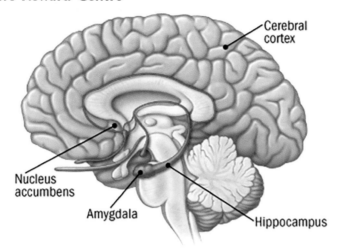

The Brain and the Pleasure Principle

The brain registers all pleasures the same way, from a satisfying meal, or shopping to a psychoactive drug. The brain's reward centre takes a distinctive route, starting from the release of the neurotransmitter dopamine in the nucleus accumbens. Neuroscientists refer to this dopamine release from the nucleus accumbens as the brain's pleasure centre.

Addictive drugs can release two to ten times the amount of dopamine that natural rewards do, and they do it more quickly and reliably. The flooding of the nucleus accumbens with dopamine is stored in the hippocampus as a pleasurable memory of quick satisfaction, similar to the hunter-gatherer remembering where to locate berries for survival, but of course the taking of a psychoactive drug is an unnatural pleasure and more damaging to survival. The amygdala is also affected. It performs a primary role in our emotions and motivations, particularly those related to survival and fear. The amygdala plays a key role in engaging the transition to dependence and maintaining dependence once it has started.

Repeated use of an addictive substance causes nerve cells in the nucleus accumbens and the prefrontal cortex (the area of the brain associated with planning and doing tasks) to communicate in such a way from liking something, wanting it and then pursuing it. This process motivates us to seek out pleasure.

'Prolonged drug use changes the brain in fundamental and long-lasting ways. These long-lasting changes are a major component of the addiction itself. It is as though there is a figurative "switch" in the brain that "flips" at some point during an individual's drug use. The point at which this "flip" occurs varies from individual to individual, but the effect of this change is the transformation of a drug abuser to a drug addict.' National Institute on Drug Abuse

Take an interactive journey to see how the brain works and what impact an injury can have at www.brainline.org. Search for: interactive brain

Ireland's Drug Problem

Our communities today are challenged with a complex drug problem that is a mix of legal drugs, illegal drugs and alcohol.

CityWide's recent survey of Drugs Task Force Community Reps identified the following drugs as causing the most problems in communities:

- Cannabis – identified by 86% of respondents
- Prescription tablets – also 86%
- Cocaine (a powder typically snorted, dissolved or injected by the user) – 66%
- Heroin – 59%
- Crack cocaine (a cocaine powder mixed, cooked and dried into a rock base, which is 'cracked' into rocks that abusers smoke) – 55%
- Head shop drugs – 41%
- Ecstasy – 35%

(Source: www.citywide.ie, 'Submission on the National Drugs Strategy 2017')

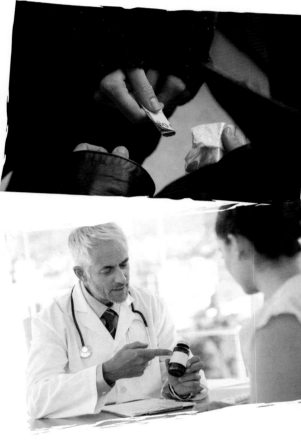

Prescribed and Non-Prescribed Drugs

Medicine is designed to help you recover from illness or relieve the pain of a particular illness. If used incorrectly it can cause harm.

Medicine can be obtained over the counter (non-prescription) or prescribed by a doctor or other health professionals. In both cases the pharmacist or health professional will ask medical questions before recommending or prescribing any medicine and they will also provide instructions as to their proper use. To avoid harmful use of medicine, treat it with respect.

R – Read the instructions carefully before taking your medication.

E – Ensure the seal is intact and that no one has tampered with the medication. Check the expiry date too.

S – Safely store and dispose of all medications. Any unused medicine can be returned to a chemist.

P – Prescription medicine is only for the person prescribed.

E – Enquire as to the effects new medication might have on other medications or food supplements you may be taking at the time.

C – Consult your doctor if you experience any unusual symptoms as a result of taking the medicine.

T – Think before you take any medication and check the symptoms associated with taking such medication, e.g. will it make me too drowsy to drive?

Drugs such as medicines for common colds and aspirin are available without prescription because they are considered a source of mild pain relief, but if used in high doses they can lead to dramatic mood changes, irregular sleep and energy patterns and false feelings of self-confidence. These are all signs of addiction. Taking non-prescribed over-the-counter drugs on a regular basis builds up a tolerance in the user, meaning more drugs are needed each time to achieve the effect. So there is a high risk of overdosing, which can cause death.

Illegal Drugs

Illegal drugs are banned substances and are therefore not regulated in their composition. This means that these drugs may contain poisonous ingredients that can cause immediate death or permanent brain damage. Ecstasy, cocaine and heroin are illegal drugs. Cannabis is recognised as causing death through accidents or suicide and is viewed as a 'gateway drug' — that is, those who try it are more likely to try other illegal drugs. Research linking cannabis use with schizophrenia is still ongoing.

DISCUSSION

1. With a partner or in small groups, and giving examples, discuss the use of drugs under the following headings:
   (a) Responsible use
   (b) Harmful use

Responsible Use	Harmful Use
1.	
2.	
3.	

Smoking

TRB

There is no responsible use for smoking as it serves no medical purpose.

TYPE OF DRUG: Tobacco
CATEGORY: Stimulant
LEGAL STATUS: It is illegal to buy or smoke cigarettes if you are under 18.

Retailers selling tobacco products are banned from displaying tobacco products and advertisements in their shop and must install a closed container for the dispensing of tobacco products. All retailers selling tobacco products must be registered with the OTC (Office of Tobacco Control).

Statistics on Smoking

- Smoking is the single largest cause of preventable ill health and premature death in Ireland.
- Approximately 23% of the Irish population are smokers — 19% smoke daily and 4% smoke occasionally
- Recruitment of new smokers continues at a high rate with 20% of those aged under 25 currently smoking.
- Women aged under 25 are more likely to smoke than men of the same age: 21% and 18% respectively.
- Three in five smokers are at least thinking about quitting; 11% are currently trying to quit; and a further 20% are actively planning to quit.
- 14% of the population have tried e-cigarettes at some point; however, only 3% still use them.
- 18% of the population in Ireland are exposed to second-hand smoke on a daily basis.

(**Source:** www.health.gov.ie, 'Healthy Ireland Survey 2016 — Summary Findings')

> What's in an e-cigarette? Why not investigate and present your findings to the class.

Over 6,000 people die in Ireland every year from smoking-related diseases; smoking is a major cause of lung cancer deaths, deaths from heart disease and deaths from bronchitis and emphysema (a disease of the lungs). Smoking can also cause diseases of the circulatory system, which can lead to gangrene and amputation. Smokers cough more, get more chest infections and experience shortness of breath.

The good news is that smoking rates in Ireland have reduced from 33% in 2000 to 19% in 2014, and we have the third lowest number of young smokers in Europe.

RESEARCH

2. **Smoking is an addictive habit. Habits are behaviour.** Young children watch their parents' or older siblings' behaviour and want to copy them. Let's question people's behaviour in relation to smoking.
   (a) Gather as much anti-smoking information as possible and create a wall display. Include facts about the effects of second-hand or passive smoking also.
   (b) Observe smoking in public places. What way are the smokers behaving? How does smoking affect the area?
   (c) Having gathered information about the harmful effects of smoking:
   • Discuss ways in which to leave situations where others are smoking.
   • Practise ways of asking people not to smoke.

What's in a Cigarette?

Cigarette smoke contains over 4,000 chemicals, including approximately 50 known cancer-causing carcinogenic chemicals as well as over 400 other toxins. Nicotine is one of the main ingredients in a cigarette and is highly addictive. Smoke containing nicotine is inhaled into the lungs, and the nicotine reaches the brain in just six seconds.

Like cocaine and heroin, nicotine activates the brain's dopamine: the reward and pleasure centre.

Some familiar chemicals found in cigarettes:
• Carbon Monoxide – car exhaust fumes
• Nicotine – bug killer spray
• Tar – used on roads
• Arsenic – rat poison
• Ammonia – cleaning chemical
• Hydrogen Cyanide – gas-chamber poison
• Cyanide – deadly poison
• Acetone – used in nail polish remover
• DDT – Insecticide
• Formaldehyde – used to preserve dead bodies
• Sulphuric Acid – car batteries
• Cadmium – used to recharge car batteries
• Diseases caused by smoking
• Cardiovascular disease

(**Source:** www.hse.ie, 'Smoking – The Facts')

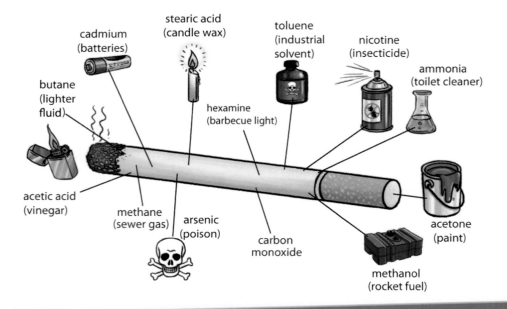

cadmium (batteries)
stearic acid (candle wax)
toluene (industrial solvent)
nicotine (insecticide)
ammonia (toilet cleaner)
butane (lighter fluid)
hexamine (barbecue light)
acetic acid (vinegar)
methane (sewer gas)
arsenic (poison)
carbon monoxide
acetone (paint)
methanol (rocket fuel)

TRB

Alcohol

TYPE OF DRUG: Alcohol
CATEGORY: Depressant
LEGAL STATUS: Intoxicating Liquor Acts, 2003 and 2008

- It is an offence to sell alcohol to anyone under the age of 18.
- It is an offence to buy alcohol for anyone under the age of 18.
- It is an offence to pretend that you are over 18 in order to buy or drink alcohol. If you are found guilty of these offences, you can be fined on summary conviction in a District Court.
- The Criminal Justice Public Order Act, 1994, states it is an offence for you to be so drunk in a public place that you could reasonably be presumed to be a danger to yourself or to anyone around you.
- The Gardaí can take alcohol from under 18s who are drinking in a public place and can subsequently contact their parents.
- The Road Traffic Act, 2010, states it is illegal to drive or be in charge of a vehicle if you are under the influence of alcohol.

What Is the Public Health (Alcohol) Bill?

The Public Health (Alcohol) Bill is legislation designed to tackle Ireland's harmful relationship with alcohol. It aims to reduce the damage that alcohol causes to individuals, families and society by reducing our alcohol consumption, with a particular focus on protecting children and young people from alcohol harm.
(**Source:** alcoholireland.ie)

Alcohol Statistics

Alcohol abuse is a problem that can affect people of any age and background when they intentionally overuse alcohol. It is a serious medical and social problem but it is not the same as alcoholism.

Alcoholism is a medical disease and people with this disease need treatment, counselling or medical attention to learn how to stop drinking and to live a healthier life.
(**Source:** Department of Health and Children, 'Alcohol and Drug Treatment Services')

In 2015, data was collected from 26 schools in Cork. The findings were:
- 83% of teenagers between the ages of 15 and 17 had consumed alcohol once.
- 37% of teenagers said they had been 'really drunk' on one to three occasions in the previous month.

The World Health Organisation's global status report on alcohol and health in 2014 showed that Ireland has the second highest rate (Austria was at the top) of binge drinking in the world. It found that 39% of all Irish people aged 15 and over had engaged in binge drinking, or 'heavy episodic drinking', in the previous 30 days.

Binge drinking for women is having four or more drinks in a single drinking episode; for men it is five or more. When you consume alcohol at that rate, your blood alcohol level gets up to around .08 or beyond, which is above the legal limit for driving. (A single alcoholic drink is the over the limit in Ireland.) You are also at a higher risk of making bad decisions, some of which could change the course of your life in a single night.

Such research illustrates how the consumption of alcohol in Ireland is often done in a harmful manner, with younger drinkers most likely to drink this way.

The findings from the Health Research Board's National Alcohol Diary Survey show:

- More than 150,000 Irish people are dependent drinkers.
- More than 1.35 million are harmful drinkers.
- 30% of those interviewed said they experienced some sort of harm due to their own drinking.
- 75% of alcohol consumed in Ireland is done so as part of binge drinking and we underestimate what we drink by about 60%.

Alcohol's Harm to Health

Alcohol has major public health implications in Ireland. The harmful use of alcohol is a factor in more than 200 disease and injury conditions, according to the World Health Organisation, such as liver cirrhosis, heart disease and cancer.

- Alcohol is responsible for 88 deaths every month in Ireland. That's over 1,000 deaths per year.
- One in four deaths of young men aged 15–39 in Ireland is due to alcohol.
- Alcohol is a factor in half of all suicides in Ireland. Alcohol is also involved in over a third of cases of deliberate self-harm, peaking around weekends and public holidays.
- Liver disease rates are increasing rapidly in Ireland and the greatest level of increase is among 15-to-34-year-olds, who historically had the lowest rates of liver disease.
- 900 people in Ireland are diagnosed with alcohol-related cancers and around 500 people die from these diseases every year.
- Drink-driving is a factor in two-fifths of all deaths on Irish roads.

(**Source:** alcoholireland.ie, 'Alcohol Facts')

Blackouts are episodes of amnesia that disrupt the ability to form new memories in the frontal cortex of the brain. Alcohol disrupts normal neurotransmission so that we lose awareness of what is going on in our physical environment and don't remember what happened to us during that particular time. That places us at higher risk of many unwanted consequences.

Excessive drinking changes your brain, which is the basis of other problems. First you lose the reward function (the feeling of pleasure) in your brain, so your reward transmitters are not working correctly, and as you keep drinking you gain activity in your brain's stress systems. Then your frontal cortex — the part of the brain that makes you who you are, makes decisions and delays reinforcement — loses the ability to work properly. If you lose function in this part of your brain then you have no brake on impulsive behaviour and stress-like responding, and that promotes a vicious cycle where you end up drinking to fix the problem that the drinking caused. Chronic alcohol abuse can cause an overall reduction in brain function and size.

Have You Heard the Term 'Standard Drink'?

A standard drink is a measure of alcohol. In Ireland one standard drink contains roughly 10 grams of pure alcohol, taking an average person one hour to process, although this varies. The number of standard drinks is based on:

- The size of the drink
- Its alcohol strength (usually shown on labels as alcohol by volume, %ABV)

1 Standard Drink **=** 1 half pint of beer/stout/ale   1 single measure of spirits   1 small glass of wine

Go online at www.askaboutalcohol.ie for a drinks calculator to help work out standard drinks, calorie content, cost and impact on health of alcohol.

Alcohol's Effect on Your Body

Brain
Damage to brain cells leading to:
- Poor memory
- Mood changes
- Learning and concentration difficulties
- Mental health problems like anxiety and depression
- Dementia

Heart
- High blood pressure and high cholesterol, causing a strain on your heart
- Weakened heart muscles
- Rapid or irregular heartbeat
- Strokes and circulation problem

Liver
- Fatty liver
- Hepatitis (inflammation of the liver)
- Cirrhosis (scarring of the liver)

Pancreas
- Malfunction of the pancreas, causing it to produce toxic substances that can lead to pancreatitis, a painful inflammation in the pancreas
- A third of people with chronic (long-term) pancreatitis also develop type 2 diabetes

Cancer
- Increased risk of several cancers, particularly for cancers in parts of the body that come into contact with alcohol like the mouth, throat, oesophagus and liver
- Even a small amount of alcohol increases breast cancer risk
- Smoking as well as drinking alcohol increases the risk of certain cancers

Stomach
- Gastritis (inflammation of the stomach lining)
- Stomach ulcers
- Heartburn (reflux)

Sex and fertility
- Temporary or permanent erection problems (erectile dysfunction)
- Temporary or permanent infertility
- Increased risk of sexually transmitted infections (STIs) due reduced inhibitions and judgement, which can lead to unprotected sex

Bones
- Weakened bones, more likely to fracture or break
- Increased risk of osteoporosis, which makes the bones softer and 'spongy'

Central nervous system
- Nerve damage
- Neuropathy, which causes weakness, burning, pain and numbness in the hands and feet

Eyes
- Bloodshot red eyes, from swollen blood vessels in the eye
- Sensitivity to light leading to migraines

Immune system
Weakened immune system, making you more vulnerable to:
- Repeated colds and infections
- More serious infectious diseases like pneumonia and tuberculosis

(**Source:** AskAboutAlcohol.ie, HSE)

DEBATE

3. Hold a class debate with some for and some against the following statement:
'If alcohol had just been discovered within the last ten years, it would be classed as an illegal drug like cocaine or heroin. You only need to read the newspapers every day to see its full effects: incidents of violence, court cases, road accidents and deaths.'

Aware

The 2nd of October is World No-Alcohol Day.

'Be a thinker not a drinker'

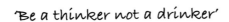

97

Cannabis

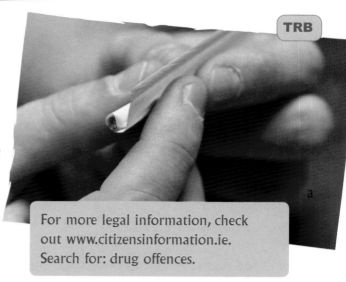

TYPE OF DRUG: Cannabis

CATEGORY: Sedative / hallucinogen

LEGAL STATUS: All cannabis products are controlled by the Misuse of Drugs Act 1984.

Cannabis is included in Schedule 1. It is illegal to grow, produce, supply or possess cannabis or cannabis resin. It is prohibited for medical and non-medical use. It is also an offence to allow one's premises (your home) to be venue for cultivating, supplying or smoking cannabis.

For more legal information, check out www.citizensinformation.ie. Search for: drug offences.

Cannabis is a plant and is used in three main forms:

- Resin, the most common form — solid dark-coloured lumps or blocks
- The leaves and stalks, called grass or weed
- Oil, which is rarely seen in Ireland

Cannabis can be smoked or eaten.

Cannabis Statistics

The results of the all-Ireland Drug Use Survey in 2016 show that the level of recent and current drug use has risen for all illegal drugs.

- The report's findings are that cannabis continues to be the most commonly used drug, with 27.9% of respondents between the ages of 15 and 64 having used it, and 7.7% having used it in the last year.
- CityWide's 2016 survey of Drugs Task Force Community Reps identified cannabis as causing most problems in communities at 86%, second highest after alcohol at 97%.

Cannabis-Based Treatments

In 2017 Minister for Health Simon Harris's proposal with the Health Products Regulatory Authority (HRPA) on cannabis for medical use announced 'a compassionate access programme for cannabis-based treatments'. This would make cannabis available to treat a number of medical conditions, despite the lack of evidence for its effectiveness and safety.

'Access to medicinal cannabis is ultimately a societal and policy decision which has to balance the lack of scientific evidence against patient-led demand,' the report by the group said.

There is a lot of misinformation in the media about the medicinal benefits of cannabis and its derivatives, such as cannabis oil, for a wide range of conditions including cancer and autism. This belief has been reinforced as cannabis has been used recreationally and medicinally for centuries. THC (tetrahydrocannabinol) in cannabis has known anti-emetic properties (meaning it's effective against vomiting and nausea), and for decades agents derived from it have been used in the clinical management of pain and nausea.

But the fact is medicinal cannabis has very limited applications. Research seeking scientific evidence to support its medicinal use is ongoing.

'Why is marijuana against the law? It grows naturally upon our planet. Doesn't the idea of making nature against the law seem to you a bit … unnatural?' Bill Hicks (American comedian and musician)

Just because marijuana grows naturally does not guarantee its safety for human consumption — think of other natural plants, such as strychnine, which are poisonous.

'Dope never helped anybody sing better or play music better or do anything better. All dope can do for you is kill you – and kill you the long, slow, hard way.'
Billie Holiday, American jazz singer

Ecstasy

TYPE OF DRUG: Ecstasy
CATEGORY: Stimulant / hallucinogen
LEGAL STATUS: Under the Misuse of Drugs Act, it is illegal to sell, possess or supply ecstasy. It is also an offence to allow one's premises to be used as a venue for preparation, supply or consumption.

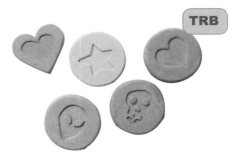

Since the head-shop ban in Ireland in 2010, people have drifted back to the use of ecstasy, Methylenedioxymethamphetamine (MDMA). The ecstasy MDMA that drug dealers are now selling is just as unreliable as that previously sold in head shops.

Some short-term effects of ecstasy
- Impaired judgement
- False sense of affection
- Confusion
- Drug craving
- Sleep problems
- Paranoia
- Depression

Some long-term effects of ecstasy
- Long-lasting brain damage, affecting thought and memory
- Damage to the parts of the brain that regulate critical functions such as learning, sleep and emotion
- Depression, anxiety and memory loss
- Kidney failure
- Psychosis
- Death

Scientific studies on the degenerative effects of ecstasy use on the brains of monkeys have shown that even seven years after a brief exposure to ecstasy serotonin levels in monkey brains have not returned to normal.

Serotonin affects most parts of your body, from your emotions to your motor skills. It is considered a natural mood stabiliser, as it is the chemical that helps with sleeping, eating and digestion. Serotonin helps to reduce depression, regulate anxiety, heal wounds and maintain bone health.

TRB

Cocaine

TYPE OF DRUG: Cocaine
CATEGORY: Stimulant
LEGAL STATUS: It is illegal to sell, possess or supply cocaine. It is also an offence to allow one's premises to be a venue for preparation, supply or consumption of cocaine.

Powder cocaine and crack cocaine both derive from certain types of coca plant. While they have similar effects and dangers (i.e. addiction, brain damage, harm to the body) the two are different substances.

Cocaine or powder cocaine is a white crystalline powder (hydrochloride salt) that is abused by snorting or by dissolving in water and injecting into a vein. This form of cocaine cannot be smoked. Powder cocaine is much more expensive than crack cocaine. Most drug seizures are of powder cocaine.

Crack is a mixture of powder cocaine, water and baking soda that is dried into solid blocks. These off-white blocks are 'cracked' into rocks that are smoked or dissolved in an acidic liquid and injected. There is a greater risk for psychological dependence when cocaine is smoked rather than snorted. Crack cocaine is more commonly associated with violence than its counterpart.

Cocaine Statistics

Every four years the National Advisory Committee on Drugs and Alcohol (NACDA) and the Northern Ireland Public Health Information and Research Branch (PHIRB) commission a survey of the general population to estimate the number of people in Ireland who use drugs and alcohol. Face-to-face interviews take place with respondents aged 15+ normally resident in households in Ireland and Northern Ireland. The 2014/15 survey involved 9,505 people (7,005 in the Republic of Ireland and 2,500 in Northern Ireland). The results for Ireland showed:

- Lifetime usage of cocaine (including crack) and cocaine powder at 6.6% and 6.4% respectively
- The percentage of respondents aged 25–64 years who reported using cocaine (including crack) at some point in their lives increased from 7% to 8%
- The proportion of young adults (15–34) who reported using cocaine in their lifetime had also increased from 9% to 11%.
- Similar to previous studies, more men reported using cocaine in their lifetime at 11% compared to women at 5%.

(**Source:** HRB National Drugs Library, 'Cocaine: The Irish Situation')

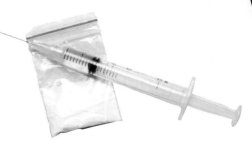

Heroin

TYPE OF DRUG: Heroin
CATEGORY: Opiate (painkiller)
LEGAL STATUS: Heroin is a controlled substance. It is an offence, unless prescribed by a doctor or pharmacist, to import, distribute, produce or supply it.

Opiates are derived from the dried milk of the opium poppy. Synthetic opiates are called opioids. Heroin is the most commonly used opioid. Methadone, which is used as a substitute drug in the treatment of heroin addiction, is also an opioid.

Heroin Statistics

- There are approximately 20,000 heroin addicts in Ireland
- The fatality rate of Irish heroin users is three times the European average
- Life expectancy of an addict is 40 years

Rachael Keogh from Dublin started using heroin at age 15. She became homeless and almost destroyed her arms from the constant injecting. She is now clean and studying at university, but her recovery was hard won. In a documentary on Drugs.ie, Rachel's Story Part 2: My Way Back, she said: 'People think when you get clean you just bounce back to normal life when that's not the case … I had to work very hard to get to a normal state on a daily basis for the first seven years or so. It took that length of time to thaw out, because it's not easy to face up to the type of life you had, you start to realise the way you've been living. It is something you have to live with — it's not just a documentary or a story: it's real life.
'Changing is the hard part, it takes years. Recovery is a lifelong thing no matter how hard you try. I'm clean but it's something I will always need help with.'

Amphetamines

TYPE OF DRUG: Amphetamines
CATEGORY: Stimulant
LEGAL STATUS: Some amphetamine-based drugs can be prescribed by doctors for conditions such as narcolepsy or hyperactivity. The Misuse of Drugs Act controls most of the amphetamine type drugs, prohibiting their unauthorised production, supply or possession. It is also an offence to allow one's premises to be the venue for same.

Amphetamines are synthetic, addictive, stimulant drugs that cause the nervous system to become more active so that a person feels more energy and mental excitement.

Some Types of Amphetamines

- Dexamphetamine, used for medical purposes to treat conditions such as Attention Deficit Hyperactivity Disorder (ADHD)
- Amphetamine sulphate, known mainly as 'speed' (powder form)
- Methamphetamine, a more potent form of amphetamine, known mainly as 'crystal meth', 'rock' or 'ice' (tablet or crystal form)

RESEARCH

4. Research how amphetamines can erode the mind and body and present your findings to the class.

These examples of webs spun by spiders given drugs by NASA scientists show how strong an effect each drug has on the behaviour of the spiders.

Typical hashish–inspired web

Web after 0.04 mcg. LSD

Web after a high caffeine dose

Web after mescaline sulfate dose

TEAM EFFORT

5. **Divide into teams. Each team will be responsible for collecting information on one drug and will share their findings in forthcoming classes.** Creating a booklet or webpage could be a good way to share findings.
The drugs to be discussed are alcohol, ecstasy, cannabis, cocaine and heroin. Legislation and statistics for some drugs have been provided in the preceding pages. A **project worksheet to** start you off is also provided on page 103.

DRUG PROJECT WORKSHEET

Type of Drug: _____

Names of Team Members: _____

_____

_____

Person 1: Drug Origin and Make Up (i.e. ingredients in the drug):

_____

_____

Person 2: Drug Short-Term Effects:

_____

_____

Person 3: Drug Long-Term Effects:

_____

_____

Person 4: Drug Treatment, Emergency Treatment and Associated Help Agencies:

_____

_____

Person 5: Appropriate Images Selection and Layout

_____

_____

---

3. Risk Taking

Who Is at Risk?

Early Exposure to Drugs, Alcohol Creates Lifetime of Health Risk
People who began drinking and using marijuana regularly prior to their 15th birthday face a higher risk of early pregnancy, as well as a pattern of school failure, substance dependence, sexually-transmitted disease and criminal convictions that lasts into their 30s.
Source: *Science Daily,* 16 October 2008

Cannabis Use by Children 'Raises Risk of Using Hard Drugs'
A recent study found that young people who start smoking cannabis before the age of 17 are up to five times more likely to progress to harder drugs or develop problems with drinking or drug addiction than those who delay experimenting with marijuana until they are older.

According to the authors, 'early access to the use of cannabis may reduce perceived barriers against the use of other illegal drugs and provide access to these drugs'.
[**Source:** *The Independent,* 'Health and Wellbeing', 22 January 2009]

REFLECTION

1. 'Ignoring the consequences of risk-taking behaviour can seriously compromise a young person's future prospects.'

What do you think this statement means?

_____

_____

_____

Risk-Taking Behaviour of Substance Use

'Go on, one won't kill you.'

'Sure it's only a laugh.'

'Take it – you'll be all right.'

WRITTEN ACTIVITY

2. Taking risks

(a) What other common persuasive statements can you think of?

_____

_____

(b) Do the comments above give you enough information to make up your mind on whether or not to try a drug?

_____

_____

(c) Are the comments true or false?

_____

(d) At this point what is your conclusion about listening to persuasive statements from others?

_____

_____

DISCUSSION

3. The consequences of risk-taking behaviour can be examined in three areas:
   (a) The personal consequences
   (b) The health consequences
   (c) The social consequences
In teams discuss the consequences of one of these areas.
Decide which words best describe the consequences of that risk-taking behaviour.

PROJECT

4. **Create a word page from your findings from the previous discussion activity.** Write the most common or most serious consequence in the largest size and the less serious or less obvious consequences in smaller sizes.

A word page can look more interesting when the words are written close together, some vertically, horizontally, thick or thin. Keeping the colours similar helps.

Cathy's Story

Me and Dave

Dave and I have been going out for two years now. We went to the same school and did our Junior Cert together. Everyone knows we are an item and I love being with him. He always makes nights out exciting and fun. We have been drinking during the odd weekend for about a year now. I could never keep up with him, but I never worried because they say men are better able to hold their drink than women.

But lately he seems to never be without a drink and smells of beer all the time. He has started to say things to me that he never said before – like I'm boring and have no sense of humour and that I've changed. I feel that he is trying to push me into fitting in with his drinking habits. He knows I don't like drinking too much and that I don't trust his new drinking friends, but they always seem to be around. Last week one of them tried to touch and kiss me while Dave was drunk and slumped in a chair. He didn't believe me when I told him and said I was probably over-reacting. Maybe if I have a few drinks tonight I might enjoy myself more and not feel so uptight.

WRITTEN ACTIVITY

5. Having read Cathy's story, answer the following questions.
(a) What are the pressures Cathy is feeling?

_____

(b) How do these pressures affect a person's feelings?

_____

(c) What are the possible safe choices Cathy could make?

_____

(d) What are the warning signs about Dave's excessive drinking?

_____

(e) Suggest ways Cathy could deal with the situation.

_____

Jamie's Story

Pat's friend

After school I spend time with my mates. We call around to each others' house and walk up to the nearby shops for something to do and maybe get a takeaway if we have the money. Other than that we sit around on walls and chat and smoke cigarettes. All of us smoke. We have a laugh together but we are getting bored doing the same old thing every night.

Last week Pat showed us some hash he had. He rolled a joint and a few of my mates smoked it. I didn't try it because I'm always afraid to try new things. My friends had a great laugh, though; they were saying really funny, stupid things and giggling a lot. They agreed to chip in together to get some off Pat's friend in school for next weekend. None of my friends are forcing me to try it, but I feel a bit weird about being around it.

QUESTIONS

6. After reading Jamie's story, answer the following questions.

(a) What are the pressures Jamie is facing?

_____

(b) How does the pressure affect a person's feelings?

_____

(c) What are the possible safe choices Jamie could make?

_____

(d) Suggest ways Jamie could deal with the situation.

_____

Drug Driving

Driving under the influence of drugs (DUID) has been a statutory offence in Ireland since the introduction of the Road Traffic Act 1961. The legal definition states that a person must not be impaired (through alcohol, drugs or any combination of both) while in charge of a mechanically propelled vehicle.

You can lie but your mouth can't
The Gardaí are now testing for drugs

In April 2017, Roadside Preliminary Drug Testing came into effect in Ireland. The oral preliminary drug test, which can be conducted at the roadside or in a Garda station, can test for cannabis, opiates, benzodiazepines, methadone, amphetamines (including methamphetamine, MDA and MDMA) and cocaine. If the Garda suspects that you are impaired to drive safely, further blood or urine tests can be taken and sent to the Medical Bureau of Road Safety, whether the preliminary drug test proved positive or negative, thus ensuring safety on the road.

- The penalty for drug driving is the same as for drink driving — a maximum of €5,000 fine and up to six months imprisonment on summary conviction.
- If you are convicted in court for drug driving you will be disqualified from driving.
- In 2016 the Medical Bureau of Road Safety tested 1,225 specimens for drugs and 800 (65%) specimens were confirmed to have a drug present.

RESEARCH

7. Research what actions you should take if someone has taken a substance and needs medical assistance. Compile the information into a pocket-sized booklet of first-aid responses to give to fellow students in your school.

4. Self-Awareness and Personal Skills

Values and Attitudes

OPINION ACTIVITY

1. Tick the Agree, Disagree or Unsure box for each of the following questions to find out what you believe.

	Agree	Disagree	Unsure
1. Taking drugs makes you more interesting and creative.			
2. Getting high makes a night out a 'real night out'.			
3. Addiction can be treated if the addict has enough will power.			
4. You can't get addicted to marijuana.			
5. Most people try their first drug from a pusher.			
6. If a drug is available without prescription it must be safe.			
7. If one dose makes me feel good, a larger dose will make me feel better.			
8. If my friend took ecstasy before and it didn't harm her, then it won't harm me.			
9. Marijuana and tobacco are sometimes classed as 'soft' drugs meaning they are not as harmful as 'hard' drugs.			
10. Drugs make people violent.			

'I first took drugs when I was 13. I took a drag of a joint. Anyone who has ever smoked hash will probably tell you they started the same way I did, with someone passing a joint around. Not wanting to be the only one not taking a drag, I took it, and it went from there. It seemed harmless enough. Soon I was doing everything the other teenagers were doing, and I was no longer innocent to the drug culture that was taking over.'

[Source: Julie O'Toole, *Heroin: True story of Addiction, Hope and Triumph*]

Daniel Radcliffe

Daniel Radcliffe, the English actor best known for his role as Harry Potter in the film series of the same name, revealed in a recent interview that he was sometimes drunk on the set in the later movies. In an interview with Sky Arts, he said that his alcohol addiction was caused by the pressures to maintain his public image.

'I was living in constant fear of who I'd meet, what I might have said to them, what I might have done with them, so I'd stay in my apartment for days and drink alone. I was a recluse at 20. It was pathetic — it wasn't me. I'm a fun, polite person and it turned me into a rude bore. For a long time people were saying to me, We think you have a problem, but in the end I had to come to the realisation myself.' (Sky Arts Interview, 2014)

   He is now living a quieter and more satisfying life. He has contributed to many charities, including Demelza Hospice Care for Children and the Trevor Project for suicide prevention among LGBTQ youth, which gave him its Hero Award in 2011.

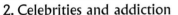

WRITTEN ACTIVITY

2. Celebrities and addiction

(a) In your opinion do celebrities have a social responsibility to disclose their experiences of addiction?

_____

(b) Should such celebrities be considered good role models?

_____

(c) Do you think some celebrities deliberately seek the attention of being an addict or go to rehab for media attention?

_____

(d) If politicians have to stand down in public disgrace over drug use, then why not entertainers?

'The road to recovery is by no means a straight one. Indeed, in my case it's been a fairly bumpy one as well. I've fallen off the wagon many times but, as a course like this shows, that's part of the recovery process.'
Paul McGrath, former Irish footballer, talking at a course on addiction studies by the Addiction Training Institute, Dublin.

RESEARCH

3. Research and discuss addiction stories using celebrities' experiences to show the downside of substance addiction.

Effects on Sexual Health

Alcohol and drugs certainly reduce inhibitions. Some people are confused by this, thinking it means becoming more fun and self-confident. Taking a drug to help you take risks is dangerous; the warning signals in your head are an instinctive response to a threatening situation. Muddling your mind through taking drugs does not help when you need to make an important decision such as deciding to be physically intimate with another person. If your mind is confused or unclear due to alcohol or drugs, another person could use your body without respect and without your consent.

It is also imperative that clear consent with free agreement is given by both individuals so that neither person is taken advantage of if they are under the influence. A person cannot give consent with free agreement if they are severely affected by alcohol or drugs, so intoxicated or high that they are incapable of understanding or mistaken about what they are consenting to. Consent cannot be given if a person is asleep, unconscious or semi-conscious. Sexual activity always carries responsibility, and sex without consent and without free agreement is sexual assault.

The Facts

According to a recent report by UNICEF Ireland:

1. 2 in 5 girls who were sexually active reported that they had drunk alcohol before their first sexual experience, compared to 3 in 10 boys.
2. 25 per cent of sexually active girls said that they had experienced peer pressure, compared to 15 per cent of boys.
3. 1 in 5 sexually active respondents stated that they did not use a condom the first time that they had sex.

'The binge drinking of alcohol in Ireland by young people has a big influence on their sexual behaviour. Comments such as, "The first time it wasn't done properly, like. It was just when I was drunk ... And I didn't remember the next morning, I was told a week later, like' were not uncommon."

(**Source:** Nicola Hayes, 'Teenage Sex Education: Ignorance and False Beliefs Must Be Banished Forever', *Munster Express Online*, 8 February 2008.

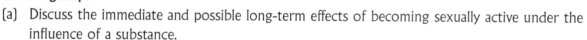

DISCUSS

3. As a group:

(a) Discuss the immediate and possible long-term effects of becoming sexually active under the influence of a substance.

(b) Suggest guidelines to improve personal safety in such situations.

5. Advance Planning

Has your point of view changed since the start of this module? It is important to know your own point of view to ensure you are making the decision you want to make, not the decision that other people want you to make.

It is easy to say 'I will never smoke' or 'I will never let myself get so drunk that I don't know what's going on.' These 'I will never' pledges don't help when the challenging situation arises unless you have prepared yourself to stand by them in advance.

Advance planning involves:
- Goal setting - Self-esteem building - Assertive communication skills - Decision-making skills

Goal Setting

Having a goal gives direction in life. Goals range from small changes you wish to make, such as 'I will eat a healthy breakfast today to help me be more alert' to more long-term goals, such as 'I aim to get enough points in my exams to study engineering in college.' Goals can be achieved by taking small steps to get to the long-term outcome.

WRITTEN ACTIVITY

1. Goals

(a)   What is your goal for your future?

_____

(b)   What experience/subjects do you need to attain this goal?

_____

_____

(c)   What steps are you taking today to start you off towards your goal?

_____

_____

Now imagine how taking an illegal drug would affect you reaching your goal. Imagine how taking the same illegal drug again and again could make your goal get farther and farther away.

How would you make a living and support a drug habit? Imagine where you could afford to live. Would you have new friends with similar interests? How important would your family be to you? How well would you look after your health and appearance?

Now imagine being offered an illegal drug and thinking of your goal and your future and answering 'No, thanks.'

'Face your deficiencies and acknowledge them; but do not let them master you. Let them teach you patience, sweetness, insight.'   Helen Keller, deaf and blind author

'Success is to be measured not so much by the position that one has reached in life, as by the obstacles one has overcome trying to succeed.' Booker T. Washington, former slave turned political activist

'Drugs are a waste of time. They destroy your memory and your self-respect and everything that goes along with your self-esteem.' Kurt Cobain of Nirvana

Self-Esteem

DISCUSSION

2. **What does self-esteem mean?** In groups, discuss the term. It may be helpful to mention comments you would expect to hear from people with high self-esteem and comments you would expect to hear from people with low self-esteem.

OPINION ACTIVITY

TRB

3. Tick the Agree, Disagree or Unsure boxes for each list item to work out your level of self-esteem.

	Agree	Disagree	Unsure
(a) Being acknowledged for doing things right is very important to me.			
(b) Looking after my health by giving my body times for activity and rest is important to me.			
(c) Admitting when I'm wrong means I can move on to the next challenge.			
(d) I like the way my body looks.			
(e) Being a winner or an achiever is how I want to be identified.			
(f) I value my uniqueness.			

A person's self-esteem is the image they have of their abilities and expectations. Without a solid sense of self, a person will be reluctant to take part in life's challenges and possibilities. Interactions with other people affect a person's self-esteem; a negative environment can threaten a person's self-esteem and development in an educational, emotional and social setting. Self-esteem is a strong internal emotion. Thousands of books have been written to teach people in all walks of life how to build their self-esteem. It is up to each person to put it into practice to gain the benefits of having high self-esteem.

DISCUSSION

4. As a class, discuss what each statement in the table above really means.

REFLECTION

5. Your self-esteem
   (a) Reflect on the statements that you agreed or disagreed with in the activities above.
   (b) What do you think is the link between self-esteem and substance use?

Self-Esteem Tips

The Dos

1. Focus on your achievements and use positive affirmations about yourself.
2. Accept compliments graciously.
3. Mix with positive and supportive people and offer your support in return.
4. Try to learn something new every day. Partake in educational learning and experiences.

The Don'ts

1. Do not compare yourself to others, their appearance and social status.
2. Be critical of media messages that make you feel bad about yourself.
3. Do not put yourself down. Use positive affirmations instead.
4. Do not compromise your needs where others can take advantage. Learn to say 'No' assertively.

Assertive Communication Skills
Saying 'No' with Confidence

You have the right to say 'No'. Saying 'No' is a way to protect our needs and rights. If you are caught off-guard and someone requests you to do something that you really do not want to do, try putting off an immediate answer. Say, 'I'll get back to you later.' If you're offered drugs, try saying, 'Not now,' and then think of how to get out of the situation.

When your mind is made up and you really know you want to say 'No', think of yourself, not others. If your friends want you to try drugs, then they are not friends at all. Do not use excuses or lies to get out of the situation but be clear in your refusal.

Try saying, 'No, I don't want to.' If the offer is repeated, repeat your answer of, 'No, I don't want to.' This is known as the broken-record technique. It prevents you from getting caught up in excuses and apologies. All methods of saying 'No' require practise. You can practise in private in front of a mirror or with a friend. Practise how to say 'No' to the small things first, like if you don't want to go somewhere with your friends. It will make it easier to say 'No' to the big things, like trying drugs.

GROUP ACTIVITY

6. With a partner or in small groups, discuss the following scenarios. Decide on a positive, active solution for each one and write it underneath.

(a) **Scenario 1:** Kate is at a party with her friend who is very drunk. She told her friend before they went out that she was not going to drink and that she didn't want her friend to drink either. Kate is tired and bored and wants to go home but her friend wants to stay. What are Kate's options and their consequences?

_____

_____

_____

(b) Scenario 2: Dave is walking home late one night in a nearby estate. He notices a small sports bag hidden down the side of a wall and decides to take a look inside it. Inside Dave finds a bundle of €20 notes and plastic bags of white powder. What are Dave's options and their consequences?

_____

_____

_____

(c) Scenario 3: Claire's sister is fighting with her mother again so Claire leaves the house because she is fed up with the noise and atmosphere. Claire calls around to her friend's house because she knows it will be quiet there. Her friend's parents won't be home until late. Her friend has another friend called Kerry there, and Claire tells them both how fed up she is at home. Kerry suggests Claire tries some hash she has in her pocket. She says it helps her relax and she starts to roll up a joint. What are Claire's options and their consequences?

_____

_____

_____

(d) Scenario 4: Neil's friend has started taking drugs lately; Neil has noticed it is all his friend is interested in. Yesterday his friend asked him for a loan of €30 but Neil told him he wouldn't have money until today. He has asked Neil again today for the loan. What are Neil's options and their consequences?

_____

_____

_____

(e) Scenario 5: Lisa hangs around with a gang and all of them except her smoke hash. She has no other friends so she hangs around with them for something to do. Today they are going to another community to buy drugs. One of her friends asks her to go with them down an alleyway to buy the drugs from the dealer. What are Lisa's options and their consequences?

_____

_____

_____

(f) Scenario 6: Tony is walking home late from a party. His friend Pete pulls up in his car and offers Tony a lift. Tony knows Pete has had a few drinks because he saw him drinking at the party. Tony has a long walk ahead of him and it is getting cold. What are Tony's options and their consequences?

_____

_____

_____

Words into Action — Coping Measures

Deciding in advance what to do in challenging situations can increase or decrease your exposure to substance use. Which coping measures do you use?

MATCHING ACTIVITY

7. Read the mock situations below and match each one to the action option that you think provides the best solution. Remember: there may be more than one action option for each situation.

Mock Situations

1. It is the last class of the school day and you just received your maths test result. You have failed again while everybody else did well. You feel humiliated and wonder what's the point in even trying!

2. Your brother is ill again and you are fed up with your family relying on you all the time to look after him. Your mother tells you that you can't go out to your friend's party tonight.

3. You are finding it hard to talk to the other people in your class. You are just not interested in the things that they talk about. School days seem to be longer than ever.

4. You just broke up with your boyfriend/ girlfriend a few days ago. During every lunch break you have seen him/her being affectionate with another person. You miss the relationship.

5. Your dad keeps checking up on your homework and study, reminding you that you won't become a doctor if you don't get the best grades. You want to do well but are feeling under pressure and your grades are starting to slip.

Action Options

A. Impulsive action

B. Listen to peers

C. Eliminate all unsafe options

D. Talk to an adult

E. Go on the offensive – standing by your beliefs

F. Seek peer support

G. Switch off and do something for entertainment

H. Keep it to yourself

I. Talk to a friend about how you feel

J. Try to reach a compromise

K. Express how you feel

Coping measures can be broken down into three approaches:

1. **Decision-making:** Thinking through the options before taking action, using problem-solving methods such as 'if I do choice A, then that will lead to outcome B'. Researching information to gather options in the early stage of the dilemma will certainly make the decision-making process a little easier.

2. **Cognitive:** Searching for information on the problem; applying reason to fully understand the predicament. Considering the emotional side of things is also used to deal with the problem. Contacting support agencies can improve understanding of all the sides and views involved in the situation.

3. **Social support:** Turning to distracting behaviour to avoid making a decision, such as meeting with peers and adults, physical activity and any type of entertainment. Self-destructive, distracting behaviour to avoid making decisions can create more problems in the long run and may lead to addiction. But positive distracting behaviour, such as meeting friends who do not partake in self-destructive behaviour, talking to a trusted adult or contacting legitimate support services, can alleviate the stress of many problems.

These coping measures suggest taking time to find out all the facts, options and support available from the onset. Those who think, analyse and find support are less likely to engage in substance-use behaviour.

Denying your emotions and turning to a substance is described as creating a crutch for yourself, a crutch that you will always turn to in similar situations. Addiction to substances can start from having poor coping skills. It's important to know how you cope with challenging situations so you can make changes now to reduce the risk of being exposed to harmful substances.

6. Relationship Skills

Peer Pressure

Peer pressure is any influence (pressure) that you feel from someone around you (peer). Peer pressure can take on many forms. People and the media use the following methods to influence people to do things that they may not wish to do or to obtain things that they do not need.

1. **Rejection:** Threatening to end a friendship or relationship. The threat of losing someone you love or like is a strong persuader to give in to pressure.

2. **Put-downs:** Nasty name-calling or insults are used to make a person feel bad.

3. **Reasoning:** Telling someone reasons why they should try something, that it will be OK if they do.

4. **Unspoken Pressure:** This is an internal pressure you feel without anyone saying anything to you. You feel unspoken pressure if you want to do the same things you see others doing.

WRITTEN ACTIVITY

1. What type of peer pressure is being used in the following statements?

(a) Have a beer, it won't kill you.

_____

(b) If you really loved me, you would sleep with me.

_____

(c)   If I eat only salads and fruit I can become as skinny as the models on the catwalks.
    _____

(d)   You're such a baby leaving the party early to go home to your mammy.
    _____

Recognising which pressure tactic is being used can help you stand up to it more effectively. However it is not always clear whether the pressure is a positive influence or a negative influence. Ask yourself these questions before making up your mind.

- **Think about your parents:** what would they say if you told them about this decision? This can give you some idea as to whether the peer pressure you're facing is good or bad.
- **Think about yourself:** does the choice you are thinking about making compromise your self-respect? Sometimes your own intuition knows what is best for you.
- **Think about the benefit:** what would you gain from the decision? For example, if a friend has been pushing you to try out for a sports team, you have the chance to get better at a skill and become more fit. If a choice seems more likely to benefit you, it may be a good decision.

Harmful Effects on Relationships

Drug users affect the lives of others, especially those they have a relationship with. Families, friends and partners are challenged in their love for the person they knew before they became addicted to drugs.

Co-dependency in a relationship can occur when one partner in the relationship lets the other partner's behaviour affect their feelings of self-esteem and self-worth. The co-dependent partner tries to provide and control everything within the relationship without providing for their own needs and desires; setting themselves up for resentment and unfulfilment. It is not a healthy relationship.

Healthy relationships exist when people maintain their own boundaries. Boundaries are needed to maintain an individual's identity, integrity, self-respect and self-worth. Co-dependent people may be unsure of themselves and have little experience of establishing boundaries. Co-dependents can take on the role of carer and rescuer to the detriment of themselves. They may think they are helping the other person but they are in fact taking over the other person's responsibilities. In doing so they encourage the person to persist in their destruction. This can lead to feelings of resentment and hurt. It is up to the co-dependent partner to decide if this is the life that they are going to lead if they remain in the relationship.

Getting Out of a Co-Dependent Relationship

If the co-dependent partner stops trying to fix, change or save the other person in the relationship, then the balance of power will change. The co-dependent person must channel their energy into standing up for themselves, set up boundaries and take responsibility for themselves only.

In other words, the co-dependent says to their addicted partner, 'If you don't change your behaviour, I will suffer from trying to change it for you.' The healthy person says, 'If you don't change your behaviour, I refuse to accept that and will leave.'

Living with addiction is soul destroying for the addict and their family. Refusing to be co-dependent to someone with an addiction is the best way to help them. Help is available to break the cycle of co-dependency.

My Addict Boyfriend

I am a 24-year-old college graduate going for my master's in psychology. I never expected the last year of my life to take the turn it has.

Months back I met someone who is and always will be very special to me. To say we got along great would be a lie. When we got along, we got along wonderfully but when we argued, we argued with the best of them. He was the only person in the world that I have ever known who was so similar to me. When I met him I knew he'd been addicted to heroin in the past. He was honest and told me his story from day one. He had spent time in state prison for his addiction. He came from a good family and was raised well. His parents went through horrors with him and his addiction that started at the age of 13. He was so against drugs I believed he really had kicked the habit.

Several months after knowing him he relapsed. The relapse started with a few small 'pick-me-up' doses and within a few weeks' became a tidal wave of addiction. He lost his job and everything else began to spiral downhill. I watched all his dreams he had built up since he got clean disappear in front of him. I became his mother. I took care of him when no one else could anymore. But taking care of him was a scary feat. I wanted him to get help but at the time that was not an option for him. Taking him to buy drugs so I didn't have to watch him suffer was a daily occurrence. Taking him to detox centres only to watch him shoot a needle in his arm was becoming frequent. I wanted to call his mother, I wanted to call his parole officer but something always stopped me. I always thought that if I did who was I? Why would they believe me? So instead of him being homeless on the street I took care of him. I falsely thought he would be ok if he did it in front of me. If he OD'ed I would be able to call 911 because I was in the right state of mind. I spent nights cleaning up his blood, washing his clothes and buying him drugs. When he no longer could afford to buy them himself I went through my bank account and then more. When his parole officer was tipped off we fled for a weekend, only to return home because we had nowhere to go. Sleeping next to someone in the throes of withdrawal was horrible. I wanted him better so bad I couldn't see how bad things had gotten. The good news is he didn't die.

However, he is back in prison now. He has spent the last 10 years of his life in and out of prison or rehabs. I keep hoping this is the last time but I don't know if it is. I don't know if it will ever be or if I will eventually be attending his funeral. All the movies in the world that depict heroin addiction don't even come close to real life. (**Source:** Heroin Awareness Foundation stories)

WRITTEN ACTIVITY

2. Having read the story above, answer the following questions

(a) Do you think this is a co-dependent relationship? If so, what are the signs?

_____

_____

(b) How has living with an addict affected the author's lifestyle?

_____

_____

(c) What is the author's attitude to substance addiction?

_____

_____

(d) Describe any opportunities there were to make safe choices in the story.

_____

_____

Addiction in the Family

Addiction threatens family life. Family members are aware of the destruction addiction causes and in many cases take on roles to cover up the signs of addiction in their home. Young people can find themselves in a situation where they have to take on a particular role to help them cope with the pressure of living with an addict. Virginia Satir worked in the promotion of treatment for children of alcoholics and she developed typologies of role behaviours in dysfunctional families. The children's roles she developed are as follows:

1. THE FAMILY HERO

This is usually taken on by the older siblings, who assume responsibility for managing the home and minding the younger siblings. Heroes are driven by shame and are usually high achievers in school. They wish to show the outside world that they can succeed. Inwardly they can feel lonely and inadequate.

2. THE PROBLEM CHILD (Scapegoat/rebel)

Scapegoats divert attention from the parent's drink problem by getting into trouble with the law or school authority figures. They are defiant and fight back and overcome their fear through anger. Inwardly they feel hurt. They do not compete but act out.

3. THE LOST CHILD

These children are characterised by silence and withdrawal and are driven by fear. Inwardly they feel lonely and unimportant. The family feel as if these children are nearly invisible and not troublemakers. They are quiet, are usually followers rather than leaders and can have difficulty in making decisions.

4. THE MASCOT (Jester)

The jester laughs at themselves and others because without laughter it would be pain and tears. For the family they provide comic relief. Inwardly they feel fearful. They may be immature and fragile and need protection. They may be anxious/hyperactive and have learning difficulties. They are escapists and often very lonely.

Most children take on a combination of roles but generally have one primary role. The family system keeps the person in the role and the role fulfils a particular need. These roles need to be understood and various approaches used so that children can move out of these roles and break the cycle of repetition.
[**Source:** Satir, Banman, Gerber and Gomori, *The Satir Model: Family Therapy and Beyond*, 1991]

> If you can relate to any of the roles above, contact the Al-Anon Information Centre.
> 5 Capel Street, Dublin 1. Tel: 01-8732699. Email: info@al-anon-ireland.org

How Can I Tell if Someone Has a Drug Abuse or Addiction Problem?

Although different drugs may have different effects on overall physical and mental health, the basic pattern is the same. Getting and using the drug becomes more and more important than anything else, including job, friends and family. The physical and emotional consequences of drug abuse and addiction also make it difficult to function, often impairing judgement to a dangerous level.

Physical Signs of Abuse and Addiction

Drug abuse affects the brain and body directly. While high, the drug affects the entire body, from blood pressure to heart rate. Stimulants like cocaine and methamphetamine 'amp up' the body, increasing blood pressure and metabolism and reducing the ability to sleep. Drugs like opiates and barbiturates slow down the body, reducing blood pressure, breathing and alertness, sometimes to dangerous levels.

Tolerance and Withdrawal

Most abused drugs are not only mentally addictive but also physically addictive. Tolerance is built up to the drug. More and more of the drug is needed to achieve the desired effect. As the body physically adjusts to the drug, trying to cut down or stop is unpleasant or even painful. These withdrawal symptoms, depending on the drug, can include shakes, chills, severe aches and pains, difficulty sleeping, agitation, depression and even hallucinations or psychosis. Avoiding withdrawal adds to the urgency of keeping up drug abuse and increases drug dependence.

RESEARCH

3. Research the physical signs of drug abuse and addiction.

Mental and Emotional Signs of Abuse and Addiction

When someone you love has a drug abuse or addiction problem

Abuse and addiction affect mood, as drugs are abused for the temporary good feelings they provide. These feelings can vary depending on the drug used. If someone you love is abusing drugs, it is an enormous emotional strain. You might feel obligated to cover for the abuser, cutting back from work to deal with the abuser's problems — or working more to make financial ends meet. You might not be able to see friends and engage in hobbies, as coping with the abuse takes more and more time. The shame of drug abuse in the family stops many family members from asking for help, instead pretending nothing is wrong. The emotional toll can be overwhelming. Children are especially sensitive.

You may not immediately realise that someone you love has a drug problem. It may have started slowly, and your loved one might also have tried to hide the extent of the drug use from you. You might have become so used to the drug abuse that coping with it seems almost normal. The realisation that there is something seriously wrong is almost too painful to admit. Don't be ashamed, and you are not alone. Drug abuse affects millions of families, from every socioeconomic status, race and culture. There is help and support available.

Understanding what is involved in recovery

You cannot force someone you love to stop abusing drugs. As much as you may want to, and as hard as it is seeing the effects of drug abuse, you cannot make someone stop using. The final choice is up to them. The right support can help you make positive choices for yourself and encourage your loved one to get help without losing yourself in the process. Don't expect your loved one to be able to quit without support. Withdrawal symptoms can be unpleasant, painful, and even deadly. While medical input is always a good idea, if your loved one is addicted to benzodiazepines or is a heavy drinker, withdrawal can be dangerous and should be done under medical supervision. Recovery will be an ongoing process.

Someone who abused drugs will not suddenly be a cured person once sober. Drug use may have been masking painful feelings that will bubble up to the surface. Many in recovery experience depressed moods for up to a year or more as their brain re-establishes from the drug abuse. Learning new coping skills to resist cravings, and how to apply them in stressful situations, is an ongoing process. Ongoing support is crucial to work through those issues.

Finding support

A good place to start looking for support is through local support groups. Listening to others with the same challenges can be a tremendous source of comfort and support. Al-Anon is a free peer support group for families coping with alcohol abuse. It may be a good place to begin, as these groups are numerous, and frequently alcohol is abused with other drugs as well. Similar to Al-Anon, there are several support groups for families coping with specific drug abuse as well. Information about these groups can be found below. Other sources of help and support include trusted friends, a therapist or a religious advisor.

(**Source:** www.helpguide.org, Drug Abuse and Addiction: Understanding Signs, Symptoms and What to Do)

Helpful Websites

www.jigsaw.ie	www.spunout.ie	www.samaritans.org	www.na-ireland.org
www.hse.ie	www.coda.org	www.al-anon-ireland.org	www.alcoholicsanonymous.ie
www.rutlandcentre.ie	www.talktofrank.com	www.thecoolspot.gov	www.allaboutcounselling.com

Invite a guest speaker, such as an ambulance driver, to talk to your class about drugs. Learning about the experiences of ambulance staff, A&E nurses or other health professionals can help in finding out what to do in emergency situations.

Drug debt is now a huge issue for Irish teens, warns leading psychiatrist. Fears of epidemic as youngsters are now in debt to drug dealers.

Irish Independent, 9 August 2015

IRISH GANGS RECRUIT CHILDREN AS YOUNG AS 11 INTO SERIOUS CRIME. RESEARCH SHOWS DRUGS, ALCOHOL AND STATUS USED TO ENTRAP VULNERABLE YOUNG PEOPLE.

The Irish Times, 13 February 2017

Gardaí investigating suspected drug related death of Cork teen.

Irish Examiner, 16 January 2017

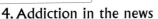

4. Addiction in the news

    (a) Research similar newspaper articles on substance addiction.

    (b) Examine the solutions proposed in each article as to what needs to be done to prevent and treat addiction in Ireland.

    (c) Examine the newspaper stories under the following headings:

        (i)   The personal implications

        (ii) The local implications

        (iii) The national implications

        (iv) The international/global implications

Crimestoppers

If you have information on drug-dealing activity in your community you can telephone Crimestoppers on 1800 25 00 25.

- You will get through to a trained operator who will ask you only for your information
- You will not be asked for your name and your number will not be traced. No one will know that you have called
- The information gathered will be passed on directly to the Garda National Drugs Unit (GNDU)

Childline

If you need to talk to someone now, Childline offers confidential, non-judgemental support. No matter what problems you're facing or where you are, someone will be available to offer you support.

- Childline is a 24-hour service for children and young people up to 18 years of age open 365 days a year
- Calls to Childline are confidential and they don't have caller ID or trace any calls
- It won't cost you anything to call Childline and their number won't show up on the phone bill
- You can also text Childline or use live chat on their website
- Phone: 1800 66 66 66; Text: 50101; Live chat: www.childline.ie

Drugs Policy in Ireland

National Drugs Strategy

The problem of drug misuse is tackled under the National Drugs Strategy: Reducing Harm, Supporting Recovery, 2017–25, which was developed following a broad and open public process of consultation across the country.

The aims of the strategy

Goal 1: Promote and protect health and wellbeing

Goal 2: Minimise the harms caused by the use and misuse of substances and promote rehabilitation and recovery

Goal 3: Address the harms of drug markets and reduce access to drugs for harmful use

Goal 4: Support the participation of individuals, families and communities

Goal 5: Develop sound and comprehensive evidence-informed policies and actions

> **TRB**
>
> Are you aware of the substance-use policy in your school?

Glamorising Addiction

Model Zoe Fleischauer developed a heroin habit almost immediately when she moved to New York in 1993, and she says she wasn't alone: 'There are a lot of junkies in the industry. It's very hush-hush.' Now clean, she blames the fashion world for glamorising the problem. 'They wanted models that looked like junkies,' she says. 'The more skinny and fed up you look, the more everybody thinks you're fabulous.'

> Supermarkets are to blame, selling alcohol for next to nothing. At least in a pub you can monitor who is drinking and refuse to serve underage and drunk customers.

> It's up to the parent to teach responsible alcohol use.

> If you increase tax on alcohol then you deter excessive drinking. Less tax money is gained from the sale of alcohol, than the amount of damage caused by alcohol to society.

> Give young people other options than going out drinking.

> We need a stronger impacting message of the physical effects of over-drinking and a stronger message of zero tolerance to binge-drinking.

The Tools Used in the Marketing of Alcohol

Consumerism plays a large role in young people's lives. Some young people believe it is the only way to gain happiness and meaning in your life. Modelling yourself on the latest trends is a strong influence on how young people construct their identity. Commercial markets, especially the alcohol industry, exploit the young person's pathway from youth to adulthood by portraying an image of fun, social ease, success and sexual magnetism.

Young people today are targeted by increased market forces: marketing, advertising, promotions, sponsorship, branding and product development.

The alcohol industry is constantly evolving to replace the old with the new, to keep pace with the instant-gratification mentality of technologically advanced youth.

To market and package the new alcohol products to appeal to young people the alcohol industry has:

- Created designer drinks, e.g. alcopops
- Increased alcohol content in products
- Designed youth-orientated packaging
- Portrayed an idealised lifestyle and image on their product, including sexualised advertising

DISCUSSION

5. With a partner or in small groups, discuss the following statement: if marijuana was legalised do you think it would undergo similar marketing strategies?

See also Alcohol on pages 95 – 97.

WRITTEN ACTIVITY

6. Influence on alcohol use

(a) Research the current policies and legislation concerning the supply and consumption of alcohol in Ireland.

_____

_____

_____

(b) How do you think culture influences young people's drinking behaviour?

_____

_____

_____

(c) How do you think entertainment and leisure activities influence young people's drinking behaviour?

_____

_____

_____

(d) Do you think young people are too exposed to alcohol advertising, so much so that they do not realise they are being influenced?

_____

_____

_____

'I wanted to write about the moment when your addictions no longer hide the truth from you. When your whole life breaks down. That's the moment when you have to choose what your life is going to be about.'
Chuck Palahniuk, American journalist and novelist

Head shops

A head shop is a shop selling paraphernalia of interest to drug users or associated with the use of drugs. In Ireland these shops are often referred to as 'smart shops' and until they were banned in 2010 they provided 'legal highs' of psychoactive drugs, which mimic the effects of illegal drugs like heroin and ecstasy. However, head shops are still legal in Northern Ireland, and until they are banned there too, they will be a threat in the Republic of Ireland. The number of casualties of these so-called legal drugs still worries professionals, who are concerned about the long term psychological effects of these drugs on the body and mind.

The EU Drug Markets Report 2016 outlines the dominant trends in the supply and distribution of illicit drugs across Europe. It reports that:

- Ireland is the most common user of these drugs
- 20% of the 15–24-year-olds surveyed said they had used 'legal highs' at some point.

This suggests that these drugs are still available in Ireland but pushed underground.

PAIRED ACTIVITY

6. In pairs, discuss the following statement using the guideline questions that follow.

The Irish government is constantly introducing new measures to criminalise the sale of various legal highs. But immediately after these bans, a new range of products comes on the market with a chemical compound that is not covered by the ban.

(a) How can you make young people realise how dangerous these new chemical compounds are?

(b) What actions can your class take to raise awareness in your school about the associated dangers of taking these 'legal highs'?

(c) Is there another method that the government could use to tackle this problem?

Back to the Brain

This module looked at how drugs cause severe side effects, especially with continued use, and these effects include brain damage and changes in the way in which the brain functions. Still some people consider alcohol and marijuana as recreational drugs. The truth is that no drug is recreational, nor is any drug use harmless. While a person can stop the progression of brain damage by discontinuing their drug use, many types of brain damage are irreversible once sustained.

Remember, your brain is amazing — don't underestimate the functions it controls: no computer comes close to your brain's awesome ability. The brain is like a control centre enabling you to think, learn, create and feel emotions as well as controlling every breath, your growth, balance and heartbeat.

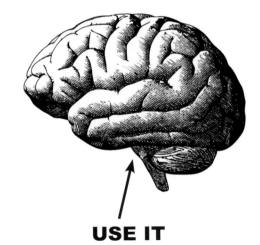

USE IT

So one of the best investments you can make is to look after your brain. The brain, like other organs, works best when the body is healthy. Exercising regularly appears to ward off Alzheimer's disease, as well as reducing body weight and lowering blood pressure. Physical stimulation of the brain can make neurons' connections stronger. To protect the neurons you already have and make new neuronal connections try such activities as:

- Learning a new language
- Listening to classical music
- Solving puzzles and brain teasers
- Eating a healthy balanced diet
- Exercising regularly — walking, jogging and cycling promote cardiovascular health.

> Use it or lose it! Think of your brain as a muscle – you need to exercise it regularly to keep it strong.

'Remember that your brain is involved in everything you do, every decision you make, every bite of food you take, every cigarette you smoke, every worrisome thought you have, every workout you skip, every alcoholic beverage you drink, and more.'
Daniel G. Amen (American psychiatrist and brain disorder specialist.)

'Happiness is not to be found at the bottom of a bottle or from the tip of a needle; it is not to be found amidst a cloud of smoke or within a sugar-coated pill. If you look for it in these places, you will find naught but despair'
Wayne Gerard Trotman (British Independent filmmaker, photographer, writer and composer)

7. Your Life Plan: How Has It Changed?

PERSONALITY TYPE

1. Circle your personality type on the right (see bird images). You identified this already in the Life Plan at the beginning of the book.

2. Your personality can directly impact how you understand, accept or reject some of the concepts in this module. What changes or challenges are ahead of you?

_____

_____

_____

3. How might you learn to deal with these changes or challenges? Think of your multiple intelligences. These may offer clues as to how you may best approach these changes or challenges.

_____

_____

_____

4. Thinking about what we've explored in this module, fill out your Wheel of Life again.

(a)   Has anything changed?   Y ☐ N ☐

(b)   If so, what has changed and why?

_____

_____

_____

_____

(c)   Do you need to take action in any area? Y ☐   N ☐

(d)   If so, what actions do you need to take?

_____

_____

_____

_____

(e)   Identify who might help you achieve these actions.

_____

5. Do you need to set a goal for this area in your life? If so, go to page 223 for a Goal Worksheet.

Module 5: Relationships and Sexuality Education

Introduction

At the centre of all your relationships, old and new, is you. Teenagers can be so distracted and misinformed by the sexual and relationship messages they receive from the media and their peers that they forget that it is still 'OK to be me'. This module focuses on recognising a sense of personal self-worth and having the life skills to negotiate your way respectfully through various relationships.

'In the past, sex and sexual health were taboo subjects. Sex is a normal part of everyday life and essential to our survival as a species. It is also good for our physical and mental health and for healthy relationships. The National Health Strategy 2015–2020 acknowledges the importance of developing a healthy attitude to sexuality in young people and of building on that foundation for positive sexual health and wellbeing into adulthood and older age.'

Leo Varadkar, Taoiseach

Looking after your sexual health and wellbeing is as important as looking after any aspect of your general health and wellbeing. Developing a positive and respectful attitude to personal sexuality and the sexuality of others and being aware of your sexual health is discussed throughout this module.

1. Self-Awareness and Personal Skills

Relationships with parents, siblings and friends are part of what makes you who you are. Your role and your attitude within these relationships can determine how smoothly the relationships work. Relationships work both ways; there needs to be give and take and mutual respect. The contribution you make in your relationships can be improved by recognising the personal strengths you already have.

Look at the list below of personal character strengths. The list is grouped into six categories of virtues (Peterson and Seligman, 2004).

> **1:** Strengths of Wisdom and Knowledge —
> cognitive strengths that entail the acquisition and use of knowledge

1. Creativity (originality, ingenuity): thinking of novel and productive ways to conceptualise and do things.
2. Curiosity (interest, novelty-seeking, openness to experience): taking an interest in ongoing experience for its own sake; exploring and discovering.
3. Open-mindedness (judgement, critical thinking): thinking things through and examining them from all sides; weighing all evidence fairly.
4. Love of learning: mastering new skills, topics and bodies of knowledge, whether on one's own or formally.
5. Perspective (wisdom): being able to provide wise counsel (advice) to others; having ways of looking at the world that make sense to oneself and to other people.

2: Strengths of Courage —
emotional strengths that involve the exercise of will to accomplish goals in the face of opposition, external and internal

6. Bravery (valour): Facing fears, challenge, difficulty or pain; acting on convictions even if unpopular.
7. Persistence (perseverance, industriousness): finishing what one starts; persisting in a course of action in spite of obstacles.
8. Integrity (authenticity, honesty): presenting oneself in a genuine way; taking responsibility for one's feelings and actions.
9. Vitality (zest, enthusiasm, vigour, energy): approaching life with excitement and energy; feeling alive and activated.

3: Strengths of Humanity —
interpersonal strengths that involve tending and befriending others

10. Love: valuing close relations with others, in particular those in which sharing and caring are reciprocated.
11. Kindness (generosity, nurturance, care, compassion, altruistic love, niceness): doing favours and good deeds for others.
12. Social intelligence (emotional intelligence, personal intelligence): being aware of the motives and feelings of other people and oneself.

4: Strengths of Justice —
civic strengths that underlie healthy community life

13. Citizenship (social responsibility, loyalty, teamwork): working well as a member of a group or team; being loyal to the group.
14. Fairness: treating all people the same according to notions of fairness and justice; not letting personal feelings bias decisions about others.
15. Leadership: encouraging a group of which one is a member to get things done and at the same time maintain good relations within a group.

5: Strengths of Temperance –
strengths that protect against excess

16. Forgiveness and mercy: forgiving those who have done wrong; accepting the shortcomings of others; giving people a second chance; not being vengeful.

17. Humility/Modesty: letting one's accomplishments speak for themselves; not regarding oneself as more special than one is.

18. Prudence: being careful about one's choices; not taking undue risks; not saying or doing things that might later be regretted.

19. Self-regulation (self-control): regulating what one feels and does; being disciplined; controlling one's appetites and emotions.

6: Strengths of Transcendence –
strengths that forge connections to the larger universe and provide meaning

20. Appreciation of beauty and excellence (awe, wonder): appreciating beauty, excellence and/or skilled performance in various domains of life.

21. Gratitude: being aware of and thankful for the good things that happen; taking time to express thanks.

22. Hope (optimism, future-mindedness, future orientation): Expecting the best in the future and working to achieve it.

23. Humour (playfulness): liking to laugh and tease; bringing smiles to other people; seeing the light side.

24. Spirituality (religiousness, faith, purpose): having coherent beliefs about a higher purpose, the meaning of life and the meaning of the universe.
(Source: www.meaningandhappiness.com)

WRITTEN ACTIVITY

1. Relationship Strengths

(a) List strengths of your own that you recognise from the list on pages 129–131.
These are some of the strengths and qualities that you bring to a relationship.

(b)   List five new strengths you desire to have.

My Strengths

1. _____
2. _____
3. _____
4. _____
5. _____

My Desired Strengths

1. _____
2. _____
3. _____
4. _____
5. _____

WRITTEN ACTIVITY

2. In the blank boxes below write **inspirational quotes** to help you work towards your desired strengths. Here are some to get you started:

> 1. If you haven't the strength to impose your own terms upon life, you must accept the terms it offers you.
> T.S. Eliot, English writer and poet

> 2. The chief executive who knows his strengths and weaknesses as a leader is likely to be far more effective than the one who remains blind to them.
> John Adair, British Author

> 3. If human beings are perceived as potentials rather than problems, as possessing strengths instead of weaknesses, as unlimited rather than dull and unresponsive, then they thrive and grow to their capabilities.
> Barbara Bush, Former American First Lady

> 4. Silence is a source of great strength.
> Lao Tzu, Ancient Chinese philosopher

5.

6.

7.

8.

3. As a class, brainstorm the situations where you might **try out your new strengths,** e.g. dealing with pressure from an older sibling.

   Your personal strengths can be the springboard for action. Many political leaders and humanitarian activists displayed great personal strength in making positive changes, e.g. Nelson Mandela, Barack Obama, Bob Geldof and Adi Roche.

2. Relationship Skills

See also Module 4: Substance Use, page 89.

Values in Relationships

The values of youth are often criticised by the older generation. 'It would never happen in my day' is a common critical turn of phrase. But some values have survived down through the ages and young people feel very strongly about them too. In the following activity you can discover your own values and what young people have in common with the older generation.

TABLE WORK

1. In the table below, complete the traditional-values list and add some modern values of which you are aware.

TRADITIONAL VALUES	MODERN VALUES
(a) Respect	
(b) Discipline	
(c) Community	
(d) Honesty	
(e) Celibacy	
(f) Responsibility	
(g) Manners	
(h)	
(i)	
(j)	

PAIRED ACTIVITY

2. With your partner or in small groups, discuss the following:
   (a) Which traditional values in the table above appear outdated?
   (b) Which values are similar for both generations?
   (c) Where are the areas of potential conflict between the generations?

Having a Positive Relationship with Your Parents

Discussions about values between parents and teens are best dealt with when both parties take time to discuss the issues calmly and respectfully. Below are some tips to establish good relations with adults and parents and to also gain respect for your transition to adulthood.

- **Be respectful:** remember it is how you would like to be treated too.
- **Practise active listening skills:** take time to take what they are really saying on board before giving a response.
- **Stay calm and focused:** do not deflect from the issue by bringing up other instances from the past.
  - Do not use name-calling, labelling or blaming to get your point across. *Remember:* it is the issue you want to discuss, not the person.
  - Aim to get some common ground or agreement, even if just to give time for both sides to think further on the issue.
- **Adhere to the new arrangements:** showing you can be trusted gives you more of a chance to make other requests in the future.

WRITTEN ACTIVITY

3. For each of the scenarios below, write how positive communication could be introduced to resolve the problem.

(a) A mother is worried that her 17-year-old daughter is not interested in meeting boys. The daughter is fed up with her mother's interference and is unsure whether she likes boys or not.

_____

_____

_____

(b) A father is refusing to allow his 17-year-old son to go to a local disco even though he promises not to hang around with his friend who was caught smoking hash.

_____

_____

_____

(c) A mother finds fake ID in the pocket of her teenage daughter's jeans. She is convinced her daughter is using it to buy alcohol.

_____

_____

_____

3. Sexual and Reproductive Health

Different Stages of Sexual Development

Understanding the changes that happen in your body during puberty will help you to understand your sexual and reproductive health. From science, home economics or religious education classes over the last number of years, you may have learnt about puberty and the changes that are taking place in your body. Revising the physical changes that occur during adolescence can make a clearer connection to the emotional and psychological developments that also occur during puberty.

Puberty: What Is It?

Puberty is the beginning of sexual maturity for both boys and girls, and both can have more similar experiences than you might think — acne, body issues and a rollercoaster of emotions such as awkwardness, embarrassment and confusion.

Puberty can also bring numerous changes that may contribute to feelings of anxiety, including body changes such as growth in weight and/or height, body-shape changes, as well as increased hormonal changes. Young people might feel the need for more privacy regarding the menstrual cycle for girls and erections and/or 'wet dreams' for boys. Coping strategies are necessary to help navigate these natural bodily changes.

When and Why Does Puberty Happen?

Everybody is unique so puberty begins at different times for each person. For most people, it occurs between the ages of 10 and 16. However, it can start earlier or later.

Puberty is the beginning of sexual maturity. Once puberty begins, reproduction is possible. Hormones are released into the bloodstream to help bring about these changes. The pituitary gland (a small gland found in the brain) is responsible for the release of oestrogen and progesterone in females and testosterone in males.

> On the bright side, female humans only have to go through puberty once. Some animals, like cats, go through the trauma of the hormonal changes of oestrus (being 'in heat') for their seasonal breeding ritual several times a year.

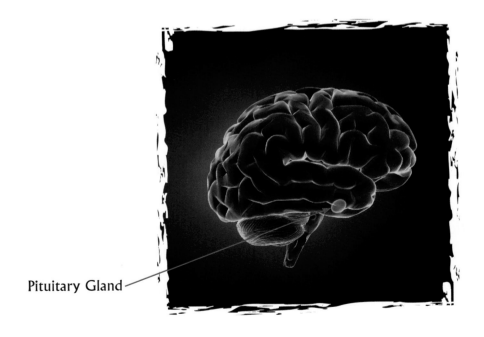

Pituitary Gland

Male Reproduction

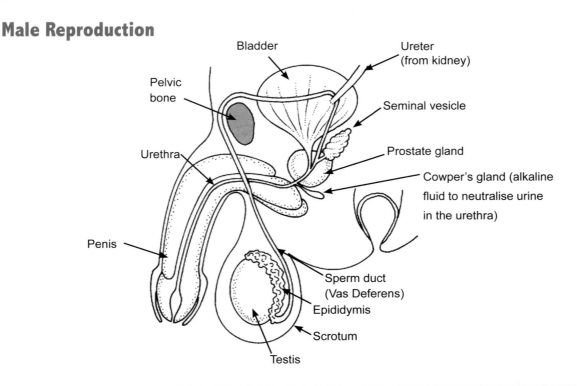

Male Reproductive Organ	What it Does
Scrotum	A sac of wrinkly skin that holds the testicles.
Penis	This is made up of spongy tissue and blood vessels. A small opening at the top of the penis allows urine out of the body. When a penis becomes stiff and stands out from the body, this is called an erection.
Testicles	These are where sperm is produced. A boy has two testicles and each is about the size of a walnut.
Epididymis	This is a small tube-like structure which stores the sperm.
Vas Deferens	There are two Vas Deferens and each one measures about half a metre. They carry sperm from the testicles to the urethra.
Urethra	This is a long narrow tube which is found in the penis and carries urine from the body. Semen also leaves the body through the urethra.

1 What is an erection?

This is when the soft tissues of the penis fill with blood and become hard and erect. Erections normally happen when a male is sexually excited. Erections are a perfectly normal function of the male body especially during puberty.

2 Will everyone know that I have an erection?

Not always. As the hormones in puberty settle down and young males advance through puberty, the frequency of unexpected erections and wet dreams should decrease.

3
What is a wet dream?
It is when you ejaculate in your sleep. Usually it happens during dreams that have sexual images. This may seem embarrassing and confusing but it is completely normal, and it happens less as boys get older.

4
Does ejaculation happen every time a male has an erection?
No.

5
What is ejaculation?
Ejaculation is when semen which contains sperm is released from the body. During sexual intercourse with a female, this is released inside the vagina.

6
How many sperm are found in an ejaculation?
Each male is different but it is estimated that the average ejaculation contains between 50 and 150 million sperm.

Testicular cancer is the most common cancer in young men aged 15–44. When detected early, 99% of those diagnosed with testicular cancer survive. To learn how to check yourself for testicular cancer, go to www.cancer.ie. Search for: check testicles.

Female Reproduction

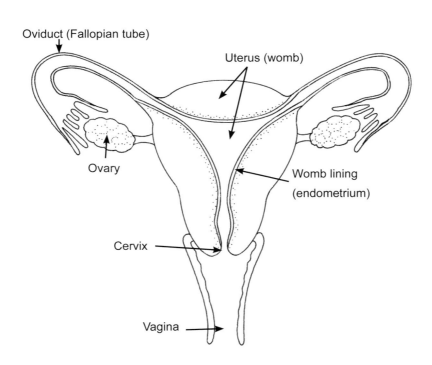

Female Reproductive Organ	What it Does
Ovaries	Most females have two ovaries. Both produce eggs. They are about the size of a large strawberry.
Fallopian Tubes	There are two fallopian tubes. These connect the ovaries to the uterus in order to carry the eggs from the ovaries to the uterus. They are about as wide as a drinking straw. Conception occurs in the fallopian tubes.
Uterus/womb	The uterus (or womb as it is called when a woman is pregnant) is a hollow muscle, which increases in size to hold a foetus. It connects to the fallopian tubes and the vagina. It is about the size and shape of a pear.
Cervix	The cervix is the opening at the lower end of the uterus and this stretches when a baby is ready to be born.
Vagina	This is the connection between the uterus and the outside of the body.

Menstruation

Menstruation is when the lining of the womb breaks down and is released through the vagina. When girls menstruate, it is usually referred to as 'having a period'. The first day of a girl's period is called day 1 of her menstrual cycle.

1 How long do periods last?

The average length of bleeding lasts between three and six days depending on the individual.

2 Do periods always hurt?

For some women periods are easy to manage; for others they can be painful. During a woman's menstrual period her uterus contracts to help remove its lining. Hormone-like substances (prostaglandins) involved in pain and inflammation activate the uterine muscle contractions. Higher levels of prostaglandins are responsible for more severe period cramps. If you do find periods painful, gentle exercise and perhaps some over-the-counter painkillers can relieve the cramps. Talk to your GP if period pains are not settling by your late teens.

3 Do other people know when a girl has her period?

Not unless she chooses to tell them. It is important to use the sanitation method you find most comfortable to stay clean and hygienic. When a girl becomes familiar with her period flow she will be prepared for more frequent changing of sanitary products on the days of 'heavy flow'. Changing regularly, even on lighter period flow days, can help prevent urinary tract infections, vaginal infections and skin rashes.

4 What if I have no period?

This can be due to having an irregular menstrual cycle, being pregnant, having a reproductive organ disorder or experiencing excessive weight gain or loss. Talk to your GP to find out what the reason might be.

5   What if my period is irregular?

Some females will experience this during puberty and before menopause. A small minority may experience this throughout their lives. Talk to your GP about this.

6   Does bleeding every month mean that I am not pregnant?

No. If you are engaging in unprotected sexual intercourse, you could still be pregnant.

7   Can I become pregnant when I am having my period?

It is possible if you confuse ovulatory bleeding with your period. Remember, if you are having unprotected sex, sperm can live in your reproductive system for three days.

8   What if my period is heavy or prolonged?

This is called menorrhagia. This can be due to a reproductive organ disorder, e.g. endometrosis. Talk to your GP about this.

9   What is the legal age of consent in Ireland?

The legal age of consent is 17 years for heterosexuals and homosexuals.

Having your period does not prevent pregnancy or protect you from contracting STIs if you have unprotected sex.

It is important for women aged 25 to 60, or who are sexually active, to undergo a cervical check, previously called a smear test. The test is a simple procedure that only takes minutes and is the most effective way to detect changes in the cells of the cervix. Find out more at www.cervicalcheck.ie. Since 2010 the HSE has offered the HPV (Human Papillomavirus) vaccine to all girls in first year in second-level schools. The vaccine protects girls from developing cervical cancer in adulthood. Find out more at www.hse.ie. Search for: about hpv vaccine

PMT/PMS

PMT stands for 'pre-menstrual tension', also called PMS, meaning pre-menstrual syndrome, which some females get before their periods are due. Many doctors believe it is linked to the amounts of oestrogen and progesterone (female hormones) dropping in the body usually a week before a girl's period starts. It is not clear why some women experience more acute PMS than others. Some women feel more emotional than usual at this time and have physical symptoms too.

Some of the symptoms are:

- Acne – excessive hormone levels can lead to blocked pores and spots.
- Bloating from water retention – fluctuations in oestrogen levels and a sharp drop in progesterone are to blame for the sensation of a ballooning belly. Remove gas-producing foods, such as brussels sprouts, broccoli, beans, cabbage, cauliflower and lettuce, from your diet. Avoid sugary and fizzy drinks. Coffee can overstimulate the digestive tract and irritate the bowels as well as dehydrate, which leads you to retain water. So it's well worth eliminating coffee too during menstruation.
- Irritability – caused by a drop in progesterone.

- Difficulty concentrating — described by some medical professionals as 'brain fog', this is caused by oestrogen deficiency, the activating hormone of the multi-tasking female brain.
- Headaches — the drop in oestrogen just before a period may contribute to headaches. Many women with migraines report headaches before or during menstruation: this is known as 'menstrual migraine'. It may be an idea to keep a diary of when your period and migraines start and consult a doctor to help you prepare in advance for your next cycle.
- Backaches — it is very common to experience back pain during menstruation. This is caused by contractions in the uterus, which radiate through the web of nerves within your pelvic region.
- Sore breasts — progesterone production peaks about a week before menstruation, causing the expansion of the milk ducts and leading to the feeling of tenderness.
- Constipation or diarrhoea — caused by the same prostaglandins that cause period cramps.
- Food cravings — avoid wheat, sugar and alcohol at this time, as they feed the symptoms of fatigue and can lead to difficulty concentrating and depression.
- Depression — the drop in hormones like oestrogen and progesterone may make you experience negative emotions more strongly. Depression and anxiety also make it tougher to fall asleep at night.
- Difficulty coping with stress — stress produces high levels of cortisol in your system, which can lead to acne, so give yourself a break to de-stress like going for a walk, doing yoga or meeting up with friends.
- Poor sleeping — female body temperatures rise between a half and a whole degree during their period. This can cause a problem because the evening drop in body temperature is one of the main biological triggers that make you feel sleepy. A warm shower or bath before bed may trick your body into drowsiness, because moving from a warm shower to your cooler bedroom will make your body temperature drop.

If any of the above symptoms are prolonged then it is best to consult a qualified healthcare professional for personalised medical advice.

> Don't let PMT rule your life: a healthy lifestyle is one of the best defences against PMT.

Ovulation: The Journey of the Egg (No Fertilisation)

NOTE: The star represents the egg travelling.

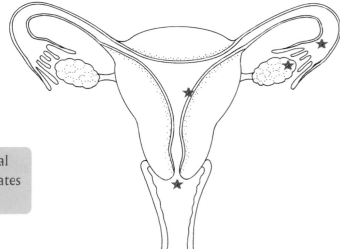

> To work out your menstrual cycle, you must have the dates of two consecutive periods.

Most females have a 'fertile period' when ovulation occurs. Ovulation usually happens from Day 11 to 17 of the menstrual cycle (counting the first day of the period as Day 1). This is when an egg (which can live for up to 48 hours) is released into the fallopian tube. If the egg meets a sperm (which can live for up to 72 hours), it is possible to become pregnant. As menstrual cycles can be irregular, particularly in adolescence, it is quite possible to become pregnant at any time if having unprotected sex. Some months can be shorter and others longer. Therefore, it is difficult to know exactly when ovulation occurs.

Making Love

Your body develops physically during your teenage years. You are not only changing physically but spiritually, emotionally and mentally. You are slowly becoming an adult. When you become an adult and you are in a long-term loving relationship, you and your partner may want to show the strength of your feelings for each other by making love (having sexual intercourse). When making love you can also conceive a baby (conception).

When you form a new relationship, it is vital that you have respect for both yourself and the other person. Only involve yourself in physical intimacy that you feel comfortable with. Remember in a long-term loving relationship both partners will care for and respect the other person's belief while maintaining dignity and respect at all times.

Conception

A baby's development is grouped into 3 stages.

Stage 1: The zygote is the first stage of embryo development after fertilisation — this is the union of egg and sperm. Conception occurs in the fallopian tube.

Stage 2: The zygote enters a two week period of rapid cell division and develops into an embryo. This bunch of cells travels down to the uterus/womb after a couple of days and begins to grow into a baby over the next 40 weeks.

Stage 3: After eight weeks the unborn human is called a foetus.

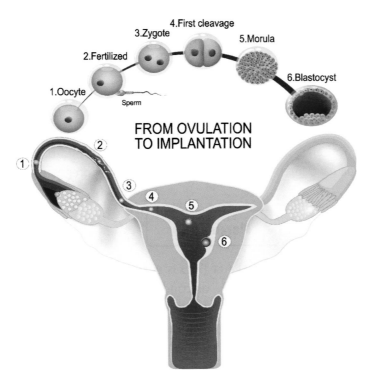

- Once conception has taken place, the characteristics that make each of us unique are formed — colour of our hair and eyes, our gender, our height.
- Throughout the pregnancy, the developing baby is totally dependent on the mother to protect it and to provide nourishment.
- If conception has not occurred, the unused egg which is released during ovulation is contained in the female's next period.

> Watch image-maker Alexander Tsiaras's TED Talk 'Conception to Birth – Visualized' at www.ted.com

Contraception

Contraception is the use of artificial or other methods to prevent pregnancy as a consequence of sexual intercourse.

Ireland's Sexual and Reproductive Health History

> **May 1971**

Members of the Irish Women's Liberation Movement travel by train to Belfast to purchase contraceptives. On their return to Dublin they challenge the customs officers at Connolly train station to arrest them for illegal importation. The customs officers allow the women to pass.

> **September 1983**

Dr Andrew Rynne is fined IR£500 for selling 10 condoms to a patient. This was the first case to be taken under the (Health) Family Planning Act 1979. Referendum on the Eighth Amendment to the Constitution is passed after a bitterly contested campaign; 53.67% of the electorate voted with 841,233 votes in favour and 416,136 against. Article 40.3.3 of the Constitution is amended to read: 'The State acknowledges the right to life of the unborn and, with due regard to the equal right to life of the mother, guarantees in its laws to respect, and, as far as practicable, by its laws to defend and vindicate that right.'

> **January 1984**

TRB

Anne Lovett, a 15-year-old schoolgirl with a concealed pregnancy, gives birth alone in a grotto in County Longford. The young girl and the newborn baby are later found dead in the grotto.

> **April 1984**

The bodies of two newborn babies are found in County Kerry. One was stabbed to death and the identity of the mother is never discovered. The other was found buried on a farm in a rural village. The mother gave birth at home after concealing her pregnancy and the baby subsequently died.

> **March 1985**

The Health (Family Planning) (Amendment) Act 1985 is enacted under Barry Desmond, Minister for Health. The Act allows for the sale of condoms and spermicides without a prescription to people aged 18 and over. However, condoms can only be sold in pharmacies, doctors' surgeries, health boards, family-planning clinics and hospitals providing maternity services or treatment for sexually transmitted infections.

> **February 1988**

The Irish Family Planning Association (IFPA) opens a counter selling condoms at the Virgin Megastore in Dublin. (Source: IFPA, 'Ireland's Sexual and Reproductive Health History')

Today there are no fines or court cases for buying contraception. Most contraceptives can be bought from shelves in pharmacies and supermarkets. All members of society are entitled to make their own decisions on their choice of safe sex practices. All couples are entitled to privacy in how they conduct their personal lives. There is a lot more sexual freedom today. The decision is in your hands. Remember the slogan:

'Nobody else is going to do the thinking for you.'

www.thinkcontraception.ie

The icons below show the range of contraceptives available for men and women. **Your choice of contraception depends on:**

- Medical history
- Life stage
- Nature of relationship

When choosing a particular contraceptive method, you must research it fully to ensure it prevents pregnancy and protects you from STIs. It is important to speak to your GP or a sexual-health professional when making this decision.

Female Contraceptive Choices

Abstinence

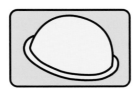
Diaphragm/cap

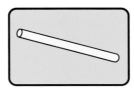
The implant

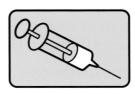
Injectable contraception

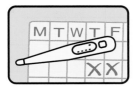
Natural methods

The patch

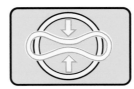
Vaginal ring

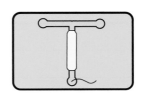
Intrauterine device (IUD)

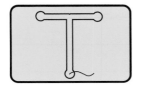
Intrauterine contraceptive device (the Coil)

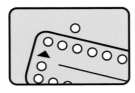
The pill and mini pill

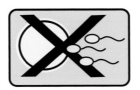
Male and female sterilisation

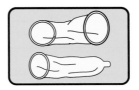
Condoms – male and female

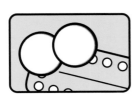
Emergency contraceptive pill (the morning after pill)

Male Contraceptive Choices

Sterilisation

Abstinence

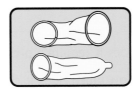
Condoms – male and female

The Morning After Pill

The morning after pill, also known as an emergency contraceptive pill, is a pill used to prevent pregnancy after unprotected sex. It can be sometimes used as a 'back-up' contraceptive. Females use it to avoid an unplanned pregnancy after having sex without using contraception or if contraception has failed (e.g. the condom slipped or the girl missed taking the pill). Emergency contraception

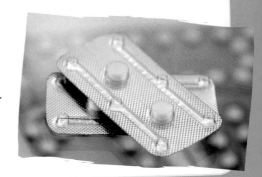

can be effective up to five days (120) hours after unprotected sex but is more effective the sooner it can be taken.

Emergency contraception is not suitable as a regular method of contraception and it does not prevent pregnancy in every woman.

Emergency contraceptive pills are available from your GP, family-planning clinic or pharmacist. Look out for the red exclamation mark sticker that signals that emergency contraception is available, through a private consultation with the pharmacist, in pharmacies nationwide.

> Remember, the morning after pill does not provide any protection from sexually transmitted infections.

GROUP ACTIVITY

1. **In pairs or small groups, research the different contraceptives available to young people in Ireland.** Use the worksheet below to help compile the information.

   Contraceptive type: _____

   Advantages: _____

   _____

   _____

   _____

   _____

   Disadvantages: _____

   _____

   _____

   _____

   _____

   Who can use it? _____

   _____

   Where can you get it? _____

   _____

   Does it require a prescription? _____

   How much does it cost? _____

Staying Safe: Looking after Your Sexual Health

The risks young people take in certain relationships can impact on them for the rest of their lives. Sexual intercourse at a young age can lead to unplanned pregnancies and sexually transmitted infections (STIs), e.g. HIV / AIDS.

Unplanned pregnancies and STIs can only be fully prevented through abstinence. Using a condom during sexual intercourse will only reduce the risk, not completely prevent it. Some STIs can lead to infertility and an increased risk of developing certain cancers.

In this section, we will find out how to take charge of our sexual health by making informed decisions.

Understanding Sexual Health

DISCUSS

2. As a class, discuss these statements:
   (a) Young people need to learn and talk about sexual and reproductive health.
   (b) Young people have the human right to sexual and reproductive health education.
   (c) Young people can contribute to youth sexual health programmes.

TRUE OR FALSE?

TRB

3. What is sexual health? Answer the true or false statements below to find out. When everyone has finished the task, the statements can be discussed to see what the general consensus is in the class.

	TRUE	FALSE
(a) Sexual health means knowing how to physically have sex.	☐	☐
(b) Sexual health is when you visit your doctor regularly and have your reproductive organs examined.	☐	☐
(c) Sexual health is taking precautions not to become pregnant unless you intend to do so.	☐	☐
(d) Sexual health is making sure that you do not share bodily fluids with someone else unless you intend to do so.	☐	☐
(e) Sexual health is only taking part in sexual acts that cannot lead to pregnancy.	☐	☐
(f) Sexual health is a private matter that you do not discuss with anyone else.	☐	☐
(g) Sexual health is being aware of methods of sexual infection and pregnancy.	☐	☐
(h) Sexual health is deciding whether to be sexually active or not.	☐	☐
(i) Sexual health is the acceptance of the functions of the reproductive cycle.	☐	☐
(j) Sexual health is a personal responsibility.	☐	☐

The World Health Organisation (WHO) has defined sexual health as:
'a state of physical, emotional, mental, and social wellbeing in relation to sexuality; it is not merely the absence of disease, dysfunction or infirmity. Sexual health requires a positive and respectful approach to sexuality and sexual relationships, as well as the possibility of having pleasurable and safe sexual experiences, free of coercion, discrimination and violence.' See also Consent, page 168 – 169.

Whose Responsibility Is It Anyway?

'A girl should never carry a condom. If I met a girl like that I would know she is up for it.'

'You can tell if someone has an infection or not. You know someone who is clean won't have one.'

'Everybody else is doing it'

'There's nothing wrong with me. I'd know if I had something, so we don't need to use a condom.'

'If you really loved me you would want to do it.'

www.B4uDecide.ie is compiled by the Crisis Pregnancy Agency. It has quizzes and information to help you make a more informed decision if you are considering having sex.

Abstinence

Abstinence is not having sex. A person can make the decision to abstain from having sexual intercourse for a number of reasons:

- they would like to wait until they are older
- they hold particular religious beliefs
- they don't want to be pressurised into having sex and then regretting it later
- they feel they haven't met the right person yet
- they don't feel ready to commit to a relationship in this way.

See also Consent, page 168 – 169.

Abstinence is 100% effective against unplanned pregnancy and contracting STIs. However, if some forms of sexual activity are carried out but not penetrative sex, some protection against STIs may be needed. Abstinence is a lifestyle choice and it is the most common choice amongst young people today, contrary to what the media and peers often state. The majority of young people are not engaging in sexual activity until at least 17/18 years of age.

If this is a decision you have made, sometimes it can be difficult to adhere to, as you might feel pressure from what you read and watch and even from your friends. But if you know this is the right decision for you at this moment, it is important that you have the courage to stick by it. Your friends and boy/girl friends should respect the decision you have made.

Are You Really Ready?

If you are considering having sexual intercourse, answer the following questions first:

See also Consent, page 168 – 169.

(i)   Am I prepared for a unplanned pregnancy/single parenthood?
(ii)   Does having sex before marriage agree with my morals/religious beliefs?
(iii)   Do I really know this person long enough to engage in an intimate sexual act?
(iv)   If I split up with this person will I still be glad I had sex with them?
(v)   Do I feel free from pressure to have sex?
(vi)   Am I sure I am not pressurising the other person to have sex?
(vii)   Do I know my partner's sexual history or am I sure there is no risk of contracting an STI?

If you answer NO to any of the above questions, then the best lifestyle choice for you is to wait or practise abstinence.

Get Your Facts Right!
*   You can get an STI the first time, or any time, you have sex.
*   You may not know if you have an STI.
*   You may not be able to tell if your partner(s) has an STI.
*   You can catch an STI more than once.
*   You can be infected with more than one STI at a time

(**Source:** www.thinkcontraception.ie)

UNICEF Ireland's 2011 report on sexual health and behaviour found:
*   1 in 5 16-year-old respondents reported that they had had sex: 82% had had full penetrative sex; 10% said they did not know what type of sex they had.
*   The majority of respondents said they lost their virginity at 16 or older.
*   1 in 5 sexually active respondents reported that they did not use a condom the first time they had sex.
*   20% more boys than girls reported that they were happy with their first sexual experience; 7% of sexually active respondents reported it as a very unhappy experience.
*   25% of sexually active girls reported they felt under pressure to have sex the first time, compared to 15% of boys.
*   Those who used a condom the first time they had sex were more concerned about getting pregnant (87%) than about contracting a sexually transmitted infection (71%).
*   The majority of 16-year-old respondents (53%) reported that they had watched pornography on the internet; more than one-third of them believed that it was accurate or educational.
*   Only 1 in 5 respondents reported they ever speak to their parents about sex.

(**Source:** UNICEF Ireland, 'Report 4: Sexual Health and Behaviour')

DISCUSS

4. Having read the facts on the previous page, do you think that Irish teenagers in general:

    (a) Are sure about the decisions they are making about their sexual behaviour?

    (b) Are well-informed about looking after their sexual health?

    (c) Are well-informed about how to avail of accurate information and advice?

Helpful Websites

www.spunout.ie
www.youthhealth.ie
www.irishhealth.com
www.hpsc.ie
www.ifpa.ie
www.thinkcontraception.ie
www.wellwomancentre.ie

He's only ever slept with one other person.

The Price of Casual Sex

TRB

1

'I have a three-year-old daughter now that I hardly ever see. Her mother is someone that I knew only for a short while before she became pregnant. I love my daughter a lot but her mother and I don't get along well so we don't live together. I feel like I am missing out on my daughter's growing up.'

2

'I had a one-night stand with a fella I met in a club. A few weeks later I had terrible pains in my groin area and had to go to my doctor. She sent me to an STI clinic and they told me I have genital herpes. They treated me but said it will come back again because I will carry the virus with me for life. I don't think I will be able to have a sexual relationship with anyone ever again.'

3

'I have been trying to have a baby with my husband for the past year. It was only when I went for tests to find out why I can't conceive that I found out that I have had chlamydia for years. I never knew I had it and now it is too late for me to be treated. I am now infertile. I had to tell my husband so that he could get treated. I felt so ashamed and embarrassed telling him.'

Sexually Transmitted Infections (STIs)

STIs are infections that are passed from one infected person to another, affecting both men and women, during unprotected sex (vaginal, anal and oral). They are caused by specific bacteria, parasites and viruses.

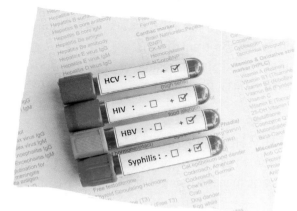

Some bacterial STIs include:
- Chlamydia
- Gonorrhea
- Syphilis

STIs caused by parasites include:
- Pubic 'crab' lice
- Trichomoniasis

STIs caused by viruses include:
- HIV / AIDS
- Genital herpes
- Genital warts
- Human papilloma virus (HPV)
- Hepatitis B
- Cytomegalovirus

The germs that cause STIs hide in semen, vaginal secretions and sometimes saliva. Antibiotics can treat STIs caused by bacteria or parasites. There is no cure for STIs caused by a virus, but medicines can often help with the symptoms and keep the disease under control. If a person is sexually active they should have regular check-ups for STIs.

In March 2017 the Health Protection Surveillance Centre (HPSC) published a provisional data report on STIs in Ireland for 2016. The report showed that:
- STIs are on the rise with a 10% increase compared to 2015.
- 70% of all STIs notified in 2016 were among those aged less than 30 years.

HIV/AIDS

What's the difference between HIV and AIDS?

HIV is the virus that causes AIDS. HIV stands for the Human Immunodeficiency Virus and AIDS stands for the Acquired Immune Deficiency Syndrome. Viruses like HIV need to infect the cells of a living organism in order to grow and develop. The human immune system will normally kill these viruses but HIV actually attacks the immune system itself.

AIDS is a serious condition in which the body's defences against some illnesses are broken down. This means that people with AIDS can get many different kinds of diseases which a healthy person's body would normally fight off quite easily.

How long does it take for HIV to cause AIDS?

The length of time between being infected with HIV and being diagnosed with AIDS depends on many different things. These days, there are a range of drugs that can be used to help people with HIV. Most doctors believe that many people can be treated for a very long time. Many people do not know exactly when they were infected with HIV, and the length of time between this happening and being diagnosed with AIDS can vary quite a lot. However in many Third World countries, where HIV rates are quickly increasing, a person can progress very quickly from HIV to AIDS.

How might you be infected with HIV?

HIV is passed on in the sexual fluids or blood of an infected person, so if infected blood or sexual fluid gets into your body, you can become infected. This usually happens by either having sexual intercourse with an infected person or by sharing needles used to inject drugs with an infected person. People can also become infected by being born to a mother who has HIV. A very small number of people become infected by having medical treatment using infected blood transfusions.

HIV cannot be caught by kissing, hugging or shaking hands with an infected person. It cannot be transmitted by sneezes, door handles or dirty glasses.

Is there a cure?

There is no cure for HIV. HIV is a virus, and no cure has been found for any type of virus. Recently, doctors have been able to control the virus once a person is infected, this means that a person with HIV can stay healthy for longer, but they have not managed to get rid of the virus in the body completely.

How can I tell if someone has HIV?

There is no way to tell just by looking at someone whether they are infected with HIV. Someone can be infected but have no symptoms and still look perfectly healthy. They might also feel perfectly healthy and not know themselves that they are infected. The only way to know if a person is infected or not is if they have a blood test.

How can I get tested?

If you feel you may be at risk of HIV, do not wait: speak to a healthcare professional as soon as possible. The most important thing is to test. Knowing that you are HIV positive is so much better for your long term health, as you can start treatment early which means you will stay healthy and well for longer. Effective HIV treatment also prevents transmission of the virus to others. So testing can improve your health and wellbeing and protect others too. HIV testing can either be done by a sample of blood being taken from your arm or using a pin prick from your finger. There are many options now for easy and effective treatment.

> Remember, you need to be tested regularly in direct proportion to the amount of sex you are having.

HIV in Ireland

Figures from Ireland's Health Protection Surveillance Centre (HPSC) show that 512 people were diagnosed with HIV in 2016. Of these 77% were male and 23% female. This figure is the highest on record and has been rising steadily since 2011.

Life expectancy in the western world for young people with HIV is now as high as 76, helped by ever-improving treatments. There is grave concern that this is contributing to people becoming more relaxed about the risk of contracting the virus. Nearly half of the new HIV cases resulted from sex between men. Nearly a fifth came from heterosexual sex. Just 4% of cases were from people who inject drugs.

In 2017 there are nearly 8,000 people living with HIV in Ireland.

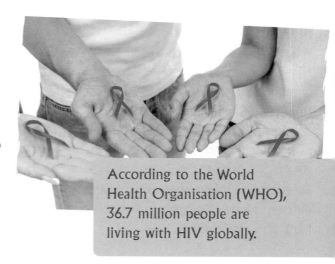

> According to the World Health Organisation (WHO), 36.7 million people are living with HIV globally.

Dubliner Robbie Lawlor, former Mr Gay Ireland has talked openly about his experience of finding out he has the disease, coming to terms with his diagnosis and his ambition to share with others how no one with HIV has anything to fear.

At age 21 he went for his first STI screening, and this test proved positive for HIV. In a 2016 interview on Independent.ie, he explained. 'I was sexually active since I was 18. 'So that was three and a half years without being checked.'

On being told he was HIV positive, he said, 'It's kind of hard for me to convey how anyone would feel about getting that diagnosis, but for me I can literally put my hands up and say I was probably the most ignorant man in Ireland, because I actually didn't know HIV even existed in Ireland.'

He went on to do a master's degree in Sexual Studies in DCU and has been involved in Plus Friends, which organises events for people with HIV, while also promoting Youth Stop AIDS, a youth-led group campaigning for a world without AIDS.

Celebrity Icons of HIV Activism

From the early 1980s to today many celebrities have lent their talents and support to raise awareness and help those who have HIV. Review the stories below of how three of these celebrities used their star power to impact the lives of millions living with HIV and their efforts to fight AIDS.

> Watch Robbie talk about his HIV diagnosis and his approach to telling people about his HIV status at spunout.ie. Search for: Robbie Lawlor his diagnosis.

Madonna

Madonna's dance teacher was HIV-positive, and when he publicly divulged that he had the virus she appeared with him at a 1989 Dance-a-Thon to support AIDS Project LA. She has continued to advocate for those who live with HIV in Africa and around the world.

'When I discovered there were over a million children orphaned by AIDS, living in one of the poorest countries in Africa, I felt an overwhelming sense of responsibility to get involved and do what I could to help bring awareness to the situation.'

Elizabeth Taylor

Elizabeth Taylor is a cinematic legend. With her humanitarian work to fight against HIV and AIDS in the 1980s she also became a global icon of activism. When Taylor was asked why she became involved so early on, she said, 'I kept seeing all these news reports on this new disease and kept asking myself why no one was doing anything. And then I realised that I was just like them. I wasn't doing anything to help.'

In 1985 she joined with a group of doctors and scientists to form the American Foundation for AIDS research (amFAR).

Bono

In 2006 the U2 frontman and rock legend Bono founded the RED foundation with Bobby Shriver to harness the power of people and companies to help fight AIDS. Bono used his celebrity status to tap into the private sector by working with major brands to create a steady flow of corporate giving into the Global Fund to Fight AIDS, Tuberculosis and Malaria. The foundation has generated over $465 million, which goes directly to finance HIV and AIDS programmes in Africa.

GROUP ACTIVITY

5. Choose STIs your class would like to find out more about. Break into groups of four, and assign each group an STI to investigate, using the standard template on the next page.

When the information has been found, each group can make a presentation to the class about their STI topic. Then all group work could be collected, copied and made into an information booklet or infographic using Canva.

Name of STI	How Is It Transmitted?	Common Symptoms	Possible Complications	Treatment	Irish Statistics
1.					
2.					
3.					
4.					
5.					
6.					
7.					
8.					

See also Module 3: Gender Studies, 1. Understanding Gender, pages 69.

4. Sexual Identity

TRB

Sexual identity consists of an individual's sexual orientation, preferences, gender roles and how they define their individual sexuality. It is important to know the difference between sexual activity, sexuality and sexual orientation.

Sexual activity: human sexual activity or sexual behaviour is the practice or behaviour with which humans experience and express their sexuality. It is sometimes referred to as carnal knowledge, coition, sex act, sexual relations, copulation or sexual intercourse for procreation between a man and a woman.

Sexuality: sexuality is our sexual feelings, thoughts, attractions and behaviours towards other people. Finding certain people physically, sexually or emotionally attractive are some parts of our sexuality. It is a diverse, personal and important part of who we are.

Sexual orientation: sexual orientation is about who you are attracted to and who you feel drawn to romantically, emotionally and sexually. It is the fact of being heterosexual, homosexual or bisexual. It is different than gender identity, which is about who you are.

Check out the 'Every Body' tool at teachingsexualhealth.ca to get a better understanding of biological sex, gender identity, gender expression and sexual orientation. The better you understand the terms, the better you may understand yourself and how you relate to other people

Our identity formation encompasses all aspects of who we are. It is continuous and influenced often by our environment and those around us. During the teenage years we start to explore who we are and who we are attracted to. Due to physical and hormonal changes, we start to notice the sexuality of others as well as our own attractions. Many teenagers find this time confusing, and they may be attracted to both sexes, which can be perfectly normal for teenagers. However some people are very decided about their sexual orientation from an early age.

The Kinsey Scale

Sexual orientation is very much part of our sexual identity and it is expansive, with a spectrum of identities. In 1948 Dr Alfred Kinsey devised a scale to illustrate this.

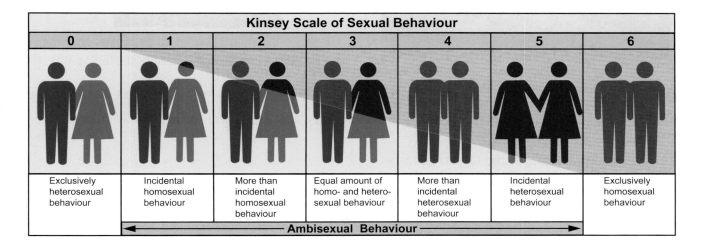

Kinsey's scale organises sexuality into a gradient scale of 0 to 6, with 0 representing exclusive heterosexuality. The numbers in between indicate varying levels of bisexuality. The scale is based on sexual experiences, and therefore each number accounts for how different instances of heterosexual or homosexual interactions imply one's sexual orientation.

Kinsey's scale is quite a simplified illustration of sexual orientation. Other complex, modern scales, such Klein's sexual orientation grid and Storm's scale, reveal that sexuality lies in a continuum, not in separate boxes, and that it can flow and change with time. However, if a person's sexuality changes it does not mean that sexual orientation is a 'choice' or 'preference' as it cannot be intentionally altered. Sexual identity is inborn, and you need not have had any previous sexual encounters to understand it.

It is just as acceptable for people to choose not to identify with or confine themselves to a single category. By accepting and embracing your and others' sexual identity, it is possible to find common ground within a welcoming and supportive community of individuals who have similar feelings, backgrounds and stories. Recognising the differences can help validate the uniqueness of all sexual orientations.

Celebrities out on the Human Sexuality Spectrum

- American singer, songwriter and actress Miley Cyrus identifies as pansexual.
- Singer Elly Jackson (La Roux) does not identify as male or female, therefore identifying as non-binary or genderqueer.
- British singer and songwriter Calum Scott identifies as gay.

La Roux

'It's only hard if you are trying to be something you are not. Being who you are is really easy.' Miley Cyrus

'It was only when I started to be myself that the music started to flow and people started to listen.'
Sam Smith

LGBTI+ Terms

Asexual: someone who rarely experiences sexual attraction. They may experience romantic or emotional attraction.

Bisexual: a person who is attracted to two genders.

Cisgender: someone who is not transgender or non-binary.

Gay: someone who is mainly attracted to people of the same gender (also described as 'homosexual')

Gender dysphoria: the distress a person experiences because the sex they were assigned at birth does not match their gender identity. They are Trans+.

Gender expression: how we show our gender through our clothing, hair, behaviour etc.

Gender identity: our deeply felt internal experience of our own gender e.g. as female, male or non-binary.

Heterosexual: someone who is attracted to people of a different gender.

Intersex: people have sex characteristics (e.g. chromosomes or genitals) that are not typically male or female or that include both.

Lesbian: a woman who is mainly attracted to other women.

LGBTI+: Lesbian, gay, bisexual, trans+ and intersex people — the plus sign represents the inclusion of non-binary people.

Non-binary: an umbrella term for people who do not see gender in a binary way. They may identify as a combination of male and female or as being beyond gender.

Pansexual: someone who may be attracted to any person, regardless of their gender.

Sex: The designation at birth of a person as either male or female based on their anatomy (genitalia and/or reproductive organs) or biology (chromosomes and/or hormones).

Sex characteristics: sexual anatomy, reproductive organs, hormonal patterns and/or chromosomal patterns.

Transgender or Trans: people whose gender identity differs from the sex they were given at birth. Trans+ includes non-binary people.

Transition: the process in which some Trans people begin to live as the gender with which they identify, rather than the sex they were given at birth. Transition may or may not include social, medical or legal changes, such as: coming out to friends; changing one's appearance and/or name, pronoun and legal documents; medical treatment, such as hormones, hormone blockers or surgery. In the past this was called a 'sex change'.

(Source: BeLonG To Youth Services)

LGBTQIA is another commonly used term in the community. **Queer** can be used as an umbrella to refer to all LGBTQIA people. **Questioning (Q)** refers to someone who is unsure of or exploring their gender identity and/or sexual orientation.

The various terms used are always evolving so a good guide is to be respectful and use the terms that people prefer.

Transgender

Transgender or trans people's gender differs from the one they were given when they were born. Transgender people may identify as male or female, or they may feel that neither label fits them.

In August 2017 President Donald Trump directed the Pentagon to extend indefinitely a ban on transgender individuals joining the military. In a series of tweets he said, 'Our military must be focused on decisive and overwhelming ... victory and cannot be burdened with tremendous medical costs and disruption that transgender in the military would entail.'

The Irish Defence Forces has since sent out a different message and says that transgender people are welcome to serve. A spokesperson for the defence forces said, '[We] welcome applications from all members of Irish society, irrespective of sexual orientation or gender. The government believes that the Defence Forces should reflect the richness and diversity of the community it serves. To that end the Defence Forces are committed to the principle of equal opportunity to all its employment policies, procedures, instructions and regulations.'

> Transgender Equality Networks Ireland (TENI) seeks to improve conditions for and advance the rights and equality of trans people and their families: www.teni.ie

LGBTI+ Artists

The arts have provided a refuge for LGBTI+ people throughout history, creating a safe space where they could express themselves and push back against conventional society, from which they'd fled. Some notable artists who expressed who they were are:

'Gluck painting in her studio, 1932.'

Hannah Gluckstein, known as Gluck (1895–1978), was an unconventional British painter. Her parents disapproved of her artistic ambitions but gave her a trust fund on her 21st birthday that allowed her to live the life she wanted. She bought a studio in Cornwall to work on her painting. She and her friend, painter Romaine Brooks, were part of a subculture that cut their hair short and wore men's clothes to communicate to those who were in the know that they were lesbian.

Francis Bacon (1909–92) was an Irish-born British figurative painter. He was openly gay and some of his paintings are extraordinarily explicit for their period, given that homosexuality was illegal in the UK until 1967.

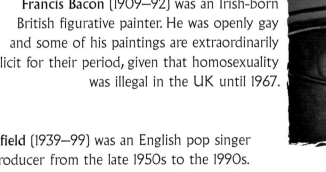

Dusty Springfield (1939–99) was an English pop singer and record producer from the late 1950s to the 1990s. In the 1960s and 1970s gay or bisexual performers knew that being 'out' could lead to a lot of negative media attention and the loss of record contracts. Though Dusty couldn't be open about who she was, she was an inspiration to young lesbians.

Will Young, British singer and actor, was told by his record company to go back in the closet. In a public declaration, he said instead, 'I'm gay and proud of it.'

> LGBTI+ sexuality was not talked about and illegal in the Republic of Ireland until recently. Homosexuality was only legalised in Ireland in 1993 – previously it was punishable by a term ranging from ten years to life imprisonment, though in practice the law was rarely enforced.

Homophobic or LGBTI+ bullying

Heterosexuality is embedded in our society and culture, and if a teenager doesn't feel they fit into this group, secondary school can be a very difficult time for them. If you feel unsure or have questions, it is important that you are able to talk to someone you trust and share your concerns or fears.

Homophobic bullying, like all types of bullying, is aimed at hurting and demeaning another individual. In homophobic bullying the person's sexual orientation is the reason for the abuse. Bullying is a conscious act which occurs over a period of time. The person being bullied feels afraid and isolated and can be subjected to aggressive behaviour. Remember: anyone who witnesses bullying and fails to take action is supporting the bullying behaviour.

Homophobia is discrimination against people who are gay, lesbian, bisexual or transgender. However people who are not gay can also experience homophobia, as other people's perception of them is that they are gay. This often happens in the school environment when someone is labelled as being gay although they may not be. This can cause huge distress for the person involved, primarily because, like all teenagers, they are forming their sexual identity so they may begin to question how they act around others, what clothes they wear etc. This can affect their self-esteem and self-confidence. Sometimes students can become depressed or self-harm due to the comments of others.

See also Module 2: Mental Health.

THINK–PAIR–SHARE

1. One of the major issues and concerns for LGBTI+ teenagers is the bullying they may receive in school. While school can be a wonderful place for some LGBTI+ students, others who identify as LGBTI+ may feel they cannot come out to their friends and family.

   (a) Take a moment to consider a person in your school who has not yet come out as LGBTI+. How do you think they would they feel? Would they be accepted or be afraid to tell others?

   _____

   _____

   _____

   (b) In pairs, with reference to the statements below, discuss what could be done in your school to support LGBTI+ students in their right to express sexual identity and sexual orientation.
   (i) 'That's so gay' has been part of the adolescent language for some time but a recent study has revealed the phrase could have deep negative consequences for LGBT students.
   (ii) 'There is a distinction between political correctness and inclusivity.'
   (iii) Marika Litz, in their talk about people not using the correct gender neutral pronouns (which is the singular they/them for gender-queer/non-binary people), said, 'Sometimes we slip up and use the wrong pronoun — and that's OK! Messing up isn't what hurts. What hurts is the repeated misgendering and lack of commitment.'
   (c) Share your thoughts with the class. As a group, draw up a list of suggestions to promote LGBTI+ ally support.

TRB

'The children who are in cots and buggies today, who will discover their sexual identity in twelve or so years' time, have the right to grow into mentally healthy and well-adjusted teenagers. What we do now can help ensure that no bully or homophobic, biphobic or transphobic culture will too easily deprive them of that right.'
Mary McAleese, former President of Ireland

'For human sympathy we all need to have stood on the outside at some point in our lives and once that has happened to you, it is very difficult to be so rigid, so prejudiced, so judgemental again, and that's how we change as human beings.'
Jeanette Winterson, author of *Why Be Happy When You Could Be Normal?*

Max's Story

I'm a 16-year-old Fifth Year student in an all boys school. I know I'm sexually and emotionally attracted to other boys. But I've never told anyone how I feel. Recently I've felt my life is a lie and that my friends don't really know who I am. I pretend to fancy girls and I had a girlfriend when I was on holiday. I've been able to do a lot of research on the Internet regarding what support there is and what organisations could help me. This has given me the confidence to realise that I'm not alone. In fact, there probably are a lot of boys in school feeling the same way. From some of the websites I've seen, many boys seem to be bullied

and can't even go to school. Luckily this has never happened to me – maybe because I play rugby and I'm not 'camp'. I ask myself every day: why can't I tell my friends or family? If they love me, surely it won't matter if I'm gay. Or will it? What would the lads think? Could I still play rugby? What would my parents think? What about me?

WRITTEN ACTIVITY

2. Imagine Max is your friend/brother/son. What advice would you give him? Give the perspective of each of the people named above.

(a) Friend: _____
_____
_____

(b) Brother: _____
_____
_____

(c) Son: _____
_____
_____

Dorothy's Story

People are very confused about me, and sometimes I wonder why they put so much energy into their curiosity. I am a 15-year-old Third Year student in a co-ed school, which I hate. I often pretend to be sick, forge notes or just don't go in. I feel most comfortable dressed as a boy, and this seems to make two students think they have the right to call me 'queer' and 'lezzer' and write stuff about me on tables and chairs. At first I was a girl who liked girls, and I even had a romantic relationship with a girl when I was twelve. But I have always known on some level that I am a boy. The best

way I've heard it explained is: 'Gender is who you want to sleep as, and sexuality is who you want to sleep with.' It took me some time to figure out the last part. I am transgender. I no longer want to be seen as female but male. I feel very isolated and can't tell anyone. I know some of the teachers have heard the name-calling but they just ignore it and keep walking by. I tried to scratch out the writing on the tables but I got caught by a teacher and was given detention for defacing school property. My family are very religious and would not be happy if I told them that I identify as male and about all the complications it is causing in school.

WRITTEN ACTIVITY

3. What advice would you give Dorothy to help them improve their situation in the follow areas?

(a) At home: _____

_____

_____

(b) In school: _____

_____

_____

REFLECTION

4. Ask yourself the following questions.
   (a) Have you ever called someone names based on their sexual orientation?
   (b) Have you ever excluded a person because you thought they might be gay?
   (c) Have you listened to gossip about another person and how people perceive their sexual orientation?
   (d) Have you ever written graffiti about a person and their sexual orientation?
   (e) Have you ever physically attacked a person, e.g. pushing, tripping etc., because of their sexual orientation?
   (f) Have you ever stood up for someone who was being bullied?
   (g) Have you ever told lies about the sexual orientation of another person?

Legislation that protects people from homophobic bullying and discrimination:

1. Safety, Health and Welfare at Work Act, 1989 (No. 7 of 1989) & 2005
2. Protection of Employees (Including Part-Time Workers) Bill, 2000
3. Unfair Dismissals Act, 1977–2001
4. Employment Equality Acts, 1998 & 2004
5. Industrial Relations Act, 1946–2004
6. Equal Status Acts, 2000–2004
7. The Gender Recognition Act, 2015

RESEARCH

5. Check out your school's policy on bullying and review its section on homophobic bullying.

How to Stop Homophobia

- Don't be prejudiced against LGBTI+ people. Some of your friends or classmates may be gay and need your support.
- Don't use the word gay in a derogatory way, e.g. 'that's so gay'.
- If you are homophobic, remember it's your issue rather than the other person's. You need to learn how to control and deal with your homophobic feelings.
- Forget stereotyping and get to know the person themselves for who they are. If it's your friend, they haven't changed at all as a person. They are just more open with you about who they are.
- If a person is gay, they don't need you to tell them they are going through a phase or that it will pass. Remember your friend has probably felt like this for a very long time and has had time to question it but they still feel the same. Accept them for who they are and feel privileged that they felt they could confide in you.
- Your friend's sexuality isn't a big joke so don't treat it as one.

If you're being discriminated against, contact a Citizens Advice Bureau (www.citizensinformation.ie), the Equality Authority in Ireland (www.equality.ie) or the Equality Commission in Northern Ireland (www.equalityni.org).

5. Parenting

TRB

The shape of the family in the Irish context has changed over the past several years. One-parent families have increased due to personal choice, divorce and separation. However, whatever shape a family takes, the parents are always paramount to its success.

Responsibilities of a Parent

- A parent should provide for their child's physical, psychological and social needs. The child depends on a parent's ability to care for them and love them. Parents should emphasise honesty, justice, loyalty and maturity.
- A parent should help their child develop warm relationships and a sense of responsibility.
- Parents provide praise, security, approval and acceptance.
- Parents help develop self-esteem and confidence in their child.

Becoming a Parent

As a teenager it is possible that you may know someone your age who has had a baby or maybe you have a baby. The majority of teenagers don't plan to have children at such a young age but sometimes this happens. The physical and emotional changes that occur to your body when you are pregnant lead to many new directions for decision-making. Decisions are now being made for 'us', no longer 'just me'. When you become a parent you will have a relationship with your child and your partner as a parent. It is important for the wellbeing of the child that you develop a positive relationship with your child and your partner. This positive relationship should continue with the other parent even if you decide to split up as a couple. You will always be parents to your child.

If you are in a relationship, or maybe you will be in the future, it is important to remember that communication is vital to the success of this relationship.

As you can see from the list on the previous page, the responsibilities of parenthood are huge. People in their twenties and thirties who planned to have a child can find it difficult to cope at times.

TABLE ACTIVITY

1. As a parent, how do you think the following needs are met?

NEEDS	MET BY
1. Praise	1. Friends, family, work colleagues
2. Security	2. Job, child benefit assistance, family
3. Self-esteem	3.
4. Self-confidence	4.
5. Honesty	5.
6. Social needs	6.
7. Physical Needs	7.

As a teenager, as at any age, having a baby is a huge lifestyle change. Look at the following table and write in the changes you think would occur in your life if you had a baby and why.

	Effect	Coping
Financial Implications	Money needed to buy baby clothes, food, equipment and pay for childcare	Getting a part-time job to pay for care
Social Implications		
Physical Implications		
Educational Implications		

I'm Pregnant

If you have taken a pregnancy test (available to buy in most pharmacies) or visited your GP or health centre and your pregnancy has been confirmed, you may be feeling a lot of different emotions, e.g. happiness, sadness, denial, anger etc. You may be worried about what people will say and about how to tell your parents.

 If you have an unplanned pregnancy, there is a lot of support available to you. Once you know you're pregnant, it is essential that you tell someone who you trust and who will support and care for you. This could be your partner, best friend, sister, parents or teacher. Remember, once you tell someone it will help make the next few months easier for you.

Case Study A

Gill is 16 years old and has just discovered she is pregnant. She doesn't have a regular boyfriend, although she is certain she knows who the father is. Gill hasn't told anyone she is pregnant. She is worried that she may have an STI and she is also worried about her schoolwork as she has plans to go to university and be a social worker. What advice would you give Gill to help her?

_____
_____
_____
_____
_____
_____

Case Study B

Megan (17) is now four months pregnant but only her boyfriend Ross knows. They went to see a doctor in a health centre and have been looking at the things they need to buy for the baby. They love each other very much, and while the pregnancy wasn't planned, they are excited about having a baby together. Ross wants to tell their parents together but Megan is terrified of how her parents will react. She knows they will go mad but she also knows she can't hide the pregnancy for much longer. Ross and Megan would like to live together so they both can be involved with the baby, as it is such a huge responsibility. But Ross is in Sixth Year and is going to college in September when the baby is due. What advice would you give Ross and Megan?

_____
_____
_____
_____
_____
_____

As you can see, having an unplanned pregnancy can create a very different lifestyle to what you imagined for you and your family. However, if it did happen, family and friends will often help and support you. There are also outside agencies to give you support if needed. It might be difficult but you could adapt your life plan to suit you and your baby. That's why it's important to think carefully about whether or not you want to have a baby at this stage of your life. The choices you make now can have an impact far into your future.

See Module 2: Mental Health, Post-Partum Depression (Post-Natal Depression), page 60.

Helpful Organisations
www.cura.ie   www.positiveoptions.ie

6 .Relationships

The relationships we form with other people throughout our lives can be a great source of enjoyment and happiness and provide an overall feeling of well-being. But sometimes relationships can be wrong for us and have a negative impact on us.

WRITTEN ACTIVITY

1. How do you feel?

(a) If I'm in a good relationship I should feel:

_____

_____

(b) If I'm in a bad relationship I may feel:

_____

_____

What Can I Do to Improve Communication in My Relationship?
- Say how you feel.
- Say if your needs aren't being met.
- Say if there are things you would like to change in the relationship.

When You Do Talk
- Listen to what the other person has to say in a respectful way.
- Don't use abusive or bad language.
- Be as honest and as open as you can whilst still feeling safe.
- Be prepared to compromise.
- Pick a good time to talk when you both have the time to listen to each other.

REMEMBER: Sometimes even after talking, relationships still don't work out. It is important for your mental well-being that you don't stay in a relationship that makes you sad, angry or unhappy, as this could ultimately lead to depression.

Good Communication:

- ensures that both parties are listened to.
- determines the quality of the relationship.
- allows you to express your ideas, fears etc. in a safe, loving environment.
- helps to develop a positive approach to solving disagreements.

See also Consent, page 168 – 169.

REMEMBER: You won't always agree on everything!

LIST ACTIVITY

2. Relationship characteristics

(a) Look at the following list and pick out the ten most important characteristics in a relationship for you.

willingness to compromise	trustworthiness	ability to deal with criticism
openness	decisiveness	loyalty
flexibility	respectful	faithfulness
honesty	selfishness	sense of humour
resourceful	impatient	moody
impulsive	ability to accept responsibility	volatile

(b) Why did you choose these characteristics?

_____

_____

_____

_____

---

7. Sexual Harassment

TRB

Harassment can be defined as continuous unwanted attention or torment. This attention can be insulting, intimidating and offensive to you. Harassment can happen anywhere. It doesn't need to take place face to face. It can be in a chatroom, by texts, email, phone calls or letters.

Harassment can include damaging your property, writing or saying hurtful or spiteful things, using images of you in a derogatory manner on a public space, e.g. on the Internet.

Text messages can be kept for up to three years by the mobile-phone provider, so if you receive abusive texts they can be located even if the person deletes them from their own phone!

REMEMBER: Harassment is illegal. To protect yourself and your family, report it to the gardaí.

Sexual harassment is when you receive unwanted sexual advances from a person or a group of people. These advances could include suggestive language, gestures or physical contact, e.g. touching. Sexual harassment can occur anywhere — it can be at work, college, a sports club, gym or a party.

How do I know if it's sexual harassment and not just someone joking around?
If the actions make you feel uncomfortable and you want it to stop but are afraid to say so, then you are being sexually harassed.

Forms of Sexual Harassment

- Unwanted physical contact with touching or slapping your bottom or other parts of your body.
- Being questioned about your sex life or love life.
- If sexual favours are asked for in return for a job promotion or you are blackmailed.
- Being teased or abused because of your sexual orientation.
- Receiving offensive or hurtful comments about the way you look or dress.
- Someone constantly commenting rudely on you or staring at you, which is humiliating or intimidating you.

See also Consent, page 168 – 169

WRITTEN ACTIVITY

1. In each of the three following situations identify:

(a) if sexual harassment is taking place (b) If so, what can be done to stop it?

(i) Mary works part-time in a grocery shop at the weekend. She is in Fifth Year in school. Her job is handy for her as it provides her with extra pocket money that she's saving for the school tour. However the owner always comments on the tops she is wearing and how grown-up they make her look. Mary feels really offended and disgusted by this but is afraid to say anything to her boss. Everyone thinks he is so nice anyway.

(a) _____

(b) _____

(ii) John plays in the local football team but hates it when one of the trainers comes into the dressing rooms as he always slaps John on the buttocks and makes some crude comment about being gay. John is extremely uncomfortable with the situation but loves playing football. He has noticed that the coach doesn't do it to anyone else.

(a) _____

(b) _____

(iii) Ciara keeps getting text messages from a guy she briefly met at a concert who insisted on getting her phone number, which her friend gave to him as a joke. But it's four months later and he is still texting her very rude and sexual messages. He has even started to send naked images of himself as well as pictures of other girls. Ciara doesn't know what to do.

(a) _____

(b) _____

Watch 'Consent, it's simple as tea' on YouTube.

What Should You Do If You Are Being Harassed?

If you feel you are being sexually harassed, it can be very difficult and frightening to do something about it — but it will help if you can tell a friend or family member who could support you.

Remember

*   You may not be the only person being harassed and by reporting it you could prevent someone else going through the same situation.
*   Let the person know that their behaviour is offensive and unacceptable.
*   Put this in writing if you can't say it face to face. Keep a copy of the letter.
*   If you are in school, college or the workplace, make your complaint to the principal/manager. If it is the principal/manager who is harassing you, tell another person in authority.
*   If it doesn't stop then make a formal complaint. In this complaint include details of the harassment and dates if you can remember. Keep a copy of the letter.
*   If the harassment is causing you stress and/or loss of sleep, visit your GP and explain to them what is happening.
*   Don't forget to talk to someone you trust. This will provide you with support.

8. Building Health Literacy

Media Messages about Sexual Activity

The media sends out mixed messages about sex. Sexual content is regularly marketed to younger children and teens and this affects young people's sexual activity and beliefs about sex. From a young age, children are bombarded with sexual content and messages such as:

*   Popular teen TV shows and ads containing sexual content
*   Pop songs containing sexual content, some including direct descriptions of sexual intercourse
*   Music videos displaying sexual situations with scenes depicting behaviours such as intercourse and oral sex
*   Teenage fashions displaying sexually suggestive words on clothing

TV, movies and music are not the only influences. The Internet provides unlimited access to information on sex. Teenagers can chat with 'cyber friends', strangers who are willing to talk about sex and teen insecurities with them. Teens may feel safe because they can remain anonymous while looking for information on sex. Sexual predators know this and manipulate young people into online relationships and, later, set up a time and place to meet.

Another false sense of sexual expression is sexting. Young people, especially girls, are led to believe that sending sexually provocative pictures of themselves or sexually suggestive texts to their friends or boyfriends is harmless fun. Such images and messages can be passed on to other friends, put on Facebook and other social networking sites and the sender no longer has any control over them. Sending and receiving such sexts can be categorised as sending pornographic imagery, which is an offence.

The consequences of any sexual activity need to be thought through before it is too late. For this reason, it is important for teenagers to see real-life examples of people who understand and deal responsibly with their sexual relationships.

Watch 'Exposed', a drama about the consequences of sending sexts, at www.thinknow.co.uk

---

REFLECTION

1. Think about how sex is portrayed in the media (e.g. music videos, magazines, films, ads, TV shows).
   (a) What is sex used for in these instances and how accessible is it to young children?

   _____

   _____

   (b) Do you have any concerns about this?

   _____

   _____

   (c) How do you think it might affect young people's attitudes to sex in their own lives?

   _____

   _____

Helpful Websites

www.childline.ie   www.webwise.ie   www.hotline.ie.
www.reachout.com (information sex and consent)

The hotline.ie website accepts reports about images of child pornography and tries to identify the source. If the material is hosted in Ireland, it will request the relevant Internet Service Provider (ISP) to remove it, in accordance with the Code of Practice and Ethics.

Moral, Social and Cultural Issues

Human sexual behaviour is governed by moral, social and cultural issues. These vary from culture to culture and country to country. These issues act as a guideline for acceptable behaviour in public and in private relationships.

Cultural issues determine the difference between appropriate and inappropriate sexual activities within a relationship. Cultural messages can be influenced by religious beliefs, such as those around pre-marital sex, chastity and abstinence.

> **Example:** In Tanzanian culture, the minimum age for sexual consent is 18 yet the age for marriage is 14 to 17 years.

Examples of moral issues that commonly arise in relationships include fidelity, gender equality, the abuse of power and premarital sex. These morals are usually learned from parents.

> **Example:** Infidelity stories about celebrities sell magazines.

Social issues are the acceptable rules within society as to what can and cannot be done. Social issues are strongly influenced by religious, cultural and political beliefs.

> **Example:** The Nice Treaty was challenged by groups such as the 'No to Nice' group, which claimed that the EU wanted to introduce 'abortion on demand' into Ireland.

Nearly all developed societies consider it a serious crime to force someone to engage in sexual behaviour or to engage in sexual behaviour with someone who does not consent. This is called sexual assault. If sexual penetration occurs it is called rape, the most serious kind of sexual assault.

See also Consent, page 168 – 169.

WRITTEN ACTIVITY

2. What other cultural, moral and social issues are you aware of in relation to sexual behaviour?

_____

_____

The Law and Sexual Activity

TRB

The age of consent in Ireland is not the same as in the UK. It is important to know the legalities associated with sexual activity. The age of consent in Ireland has remained 17 years of age since 1935. Laws change to reflect the changes in society, so it is best to get the most up to date information to help you fully understand where you stand in relation to the law.

Sexual Health Services

Information on sexual health services can be obtained from your local GP or a school guidance counsellor. Both professionals will offer advice and support. It is helpful to know other local services for sexual health and well-being for young people.

TABLE ACTIVITY

3. In the charts below, list (a) three local and (b) three national services for young people regarding sexual health and well-being. This will create a resource list for your classmates and friends.

(a) Local Services

Name			
Service Provided			
Phone number			
Email address			
Website			
Address			

(b) National Services

Name			
Service Provided			
Phone number			
Email address			
Website			
Address			

9. Consent

What is consent? Is it necessary? How can we model it in our daily lives?

Sometimes when people ask us to do something we say yes – e.g. going to a friend's birthday party. Sometimes we might say yes to the invitation, but then on the night of the birthday change our mind and say no. Sometimes we might go to the birthday party and stay a short time but then decide no and go home. Likewise, we sometimes consent to things we don't really want to do for another reason – e.g. your aunt asks you to babysit and, although you have homework to do, you say yes as you are saving up to buy a new pair of runners and the money will be useful.

There are other times when we say yes to something that we don't want to do because we don't know how to stand up for ourselves and say no. This can happen sometimes in serious situations – e.g. drinking alcohol, taking drugs, stealing or having sex without consent (rape).

Consent in a relationship involves both parties agreeing and wanting to do the same thing at the same time. Consent needs to be explicit, the absence of a NO is not a YES.

What Is Consent?

Consent is:

- **Clear** – both parties are aware of the situation and it is expressed through actions and words.
- **Coherent** – a rational, reasonable decision, and the person giving it is not impaired by drugs or alcohol. A person asleep or unconscious is vulnerable and not able to give consent.
- **Willing** – both parties must be willing to engage in the activity. There should be no pressure or coercion to engage in sexual activity. Manipulating the situation through physical and / or emotional abuse is not consent. People need to feel they have a choice and can say yes or no.
- **Process** – every time a person engages in sexual activity consent needs to be given. Just because a person says yes once doesn't mean it applies for the future. It is for the here-and-now situation only.

> Watch 'Consent, it's simple as tea' on YouTube.

A legal definition of consent to a sexual act was signed into Irish law in 2017. The Criminal Law (Sexual Offences) Act 2017 states that:

- A person consents to a sexual act if he or she freely and voluntarily agrees to engage in that act.
- A person does not consent to a sexual act if they are asleep, unconscious or incapable of consenting as a result of intoxication through drugs or alcohol.

In Ireland the legal age of consent is 17 years old for everyone. The person you are with has to give consent. Non-consensual sexual activity (anything from kissing to penetration) is against the law. (www.reachout.com)

> Remember, sexual activity without consent is sexual assault.

TABLE ACTIVITY

I. In the table below, state whether you agree or disagree with the statements about consent and ex
plain why.

Consent is ...	Agree/Disagree	Why?
(a) Required before any sexual contact		
(b) Something that both people must give and be able to give		
(c) Making sure the other person says they want to have sexual contact		
(d) Something that must be asked for every time		
(e) Saying 'I'm not so sure'/'I suppose so'		
(f) All of the above		

Consent sounds like:
- This is OK
- Absolutely
- Yes
- I like that
- For sure
- Of course

Consent does not sound like:
- I'm not ready
- Not tonight
- No
- I'm not sure
- Stop
- I suppose so

Being in a loving, healthy relationship can be a really exciting and special time. Therefore, it is essential at
all times to communicate and respect your partner's decisions regarding sexual intimacy.

10. Your Life Plan: How Has It Changed?

PERSONALITY TYPE

1.   Circle your personality type below. You identified this already in the Life Plan at the beginning of the book.

2.   Your personality can directly impact how you understand, accept or reject some of the concepts in this module. What changes or challenges are ahead of you?

_____

_____

_____

3.   How might you learn to deal with these changes or challenges? Think of your multiple intelligences. These may offer clues as to how you may best approach these changes or challenges.

_____

_____

_____

REALITY CHECK

4. Thinking about what we've explored in this module, fill out your Wheel of Life again.

(a)   Has anything changed?   Y ☐   N ☐

(b)   If so, what has changed and why?

_____

_____

(c)   Do you need to take action in any area? Y ☐   N ☐

(d)   If so, what actions do you need to take?

_____

_____

_____

(e)   Identify who might help you achieve these actions.

_____

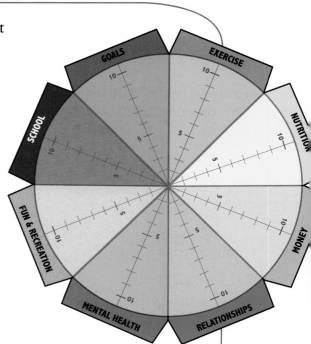

GOALS

5. Do you need to set a goal for this area in your life? If so, go to page 223 for a Goal Worksheet.

Module 6: Physical Activity and Nutrition

Active

1. Physical Activity

Physical activity has many health benefits. These benefits apply to people of all ages and races. For example, physical activity helps you maintain a healthy weight and makes it easier to do daily tasks, such as climbing stairs and walking to school. Physically active adults are at lower risk for depression and decline in cognitive function (thinking, learning and judgement skills) as they get older. Physically active children and teenagers may have fewer symptoms of depression than their peers. Physical activity also lowers your risk for many diseases, such as coronary heart disease, diabetes and cancer.

Yet, for some reason, many people in Ireland do not exercise. According to a 2015 report by the Central Statistics Office, nearly 30% of Irish people are not physically active.

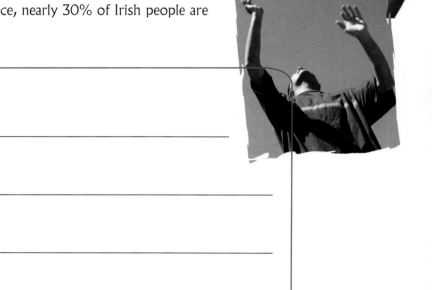

DEFINE

1. What is the definition of:

(a) Health

_____

(b) Physical activity?

_____

(c) Exercise?

_____

(d) Fitness?

_____

RAPID FIRE ACTIVITY

2. What does health mean to you? Say the first thing that comes into your head. Then see if it is listed below:

Not having to take medication

Being happy

Having energy

Being a healthy weight

Being employed

Not feeling stressed

Exercising regularly

Not smoking

Getting enough sleep

Having a healthy balanced diet

Drinking in moderation or not drinking at all

Being able to adapt to new situations easily

Having friends

DESIGN ACTIVITY

3. Design your own health symbol and explain your choice of image to the class. Write a description of the logo, the significance of the colour you used etc.

RESEARCH

4. What does it mean to be healthy?
In groups of no more than three, examine newspapers/magazines for articles that are concerned with the meaning of health.
Discuss the articles you find in groups.

Health Indicators

A health indicator is a measure that shows (indicates) the health of people in a specific population, e.g. tobacco use amongst the Irish population. Leading Health Indicators (LHIs) are measures used across the world to measure the health of a population.

THINK, PAIR, SHARE

TRB

5. There are ten Leading Health Indicators (LHIs) including:
- Overweight and Obesity
- Physical Activity
- Substance Use.
(a) In pairs, try to name the other seven.
(b) Discuss how these ten LHIs might affect your health?

> A person becomes physically fit through physical activity.

Clearly, physical activity is one of the major LHIs. It is important that you understand how much physical activity you must do in order to be healthy throughout your life. You will see that physical activity has strong links with the concepts of fitness and health.

Physical Fitness and Health

GROUP ACTIVITY

6. Take a photograph or look through some magazines, newspapers or journals for an image which represents physical activity to you. Try to use an image showing a person roughly your own age. Bring it into class. Be prepared to listen to other people's interpretation of your photo and to share with the class why you chose it.

It is important to understand what physical fitness means.
Physical fitness is made up of two main areas:
- **General fitness:** a state of physical health and well-being. This is also called health-related physical fitness.
- **Specific fitness:** based on a person's ability to perform specific aspects of sports or occupations/jobs. This is also called skill-related physical fitness.

> If you are physically fit, you are free from illness, able to function efficiently and effectively, able to enjoy leisure time and can cope with emergencies.

These two areas are further divided into components or parts.

	Health-Related Physical Fitness	Skill-Related Physical Fitness
Components	Cardiovascular endurance	Agility
	Muscular strength	Balance
	Flexibility	Coordination
	Muscular endurance	Power
	Body composition	Reaction timer
		Speed

WRITTEN ACTIVITY

7. Components

(a) For each of the following health-related fitness components, list an activity that might improve it. The first one has been done for you.

(i) Cardiovascular Endurance

Cardiovascular endurance is the ability of the lungs to provide oxygen to the muscles for continuous exercise over a prolonged period of time.

Activities? Running, walking and cycling

(ii) Muscular Strength

This is the ability of a muscle or a muscle group to exert maximum force against a heavy resistance.

Activities? _____

(iii) Flexibility

Flexibility is the measure of free movement in a person's joints, e.g. knees.

Activities? _____

(iv) Muscular Endurance

Muscular endurance is the ability of a muscle or a muscle group to exert a force repeatedly.

Activities? _____

(v) Body Composition

Body composition is a measure of muscle, bone, fat and other tissues which make up the human body.

Activities? _____

(b) For each of the following skill-related fitness components, pick a sport or occupation that requires this component. The first one has been done for you.

(i) Agility

The ability to quickly and accurately change the direction of the whole body in space. It is a combination of speed and coordination.

Activities? Soccer

(ii) Balance

The ability to maintain equilibrium while stationary or moving.

Activities? _____

(iii) Coordination

The ability to use the senses and body parts in order to perform moves smoothly and accurately.

Activities? _____

(iv) Power

The amount of force a muscle can exert.

Activities? _____

(v) Reaction Time

The ability to respond quickly to stimuli.

Activities? _____

(vi) Speed

The amount of time it takes the body to perform specific tasks.

Activities? _____

2. Mini Health- and Skill-Related Fitness Tests

Corbin and Lindsay's (2008) Health- and Skill-Related Fitness Tests

Standing Long Jump: Stand with the toes behind a line. Without using a run or hop step, jump as far as possible. To pass, men must jump their height plus 15 centimetres (six inches). Women must jump their height only.

Fitness Aspect: Power

Pass: Yes____ / No____

Paper ball pickup: Place two wadded paper balls on the floor five feet away. Run, pick up the first ball and return both feet behind the starting line. Repeat with the second ball. Finish in five seconds.

Fitness Aspect: Agility

Pass: Yes____ / No____

Paper drop: Have a partner hold a sheet of notebook paper so that the side edge is between your thumb and index finger about the width of your hand from the top of the page. When your partner drops the paper, catch it before it slips through the thumb and finger. Do not move your hand lower to catch the paper.

Fitness Aspect: Reaction time

Pass: Yes____ / No____

Double heel click: With the feet apart, jump up and tap the heels together twice before you hit the ground. You must land with your feet at least three feet apart.

Fitness Aspect: Speed

Pass: Yes_____ / No_____

Paper ball bounce: Wad up a sheet of notebook paper into a ball. Bounce the ball back and forth between the right and left hands. Keep the hands open and palms up. Bounce the ball three times with each hand (six times in total), alternating hands for each bounce.

Fitness Aspect: Coordination

Pass: Yes____ / No_____

Run in place: Run in place for one and a half minutes (120 steps per minute). Rest for one minute and count the heart rate for thirty seconds. A heart rate of 60 or lower passes. A step is counted each time the right foot hits the floor.

Fitness Aspect: Cardiovascular fitness

Pass: Yes____ / No_____

Toe touch: Sit on the floor with your feet against a wall. Keep the feet together and the knees straight. Bend forward at the hips. After three warm-up trials, reach forward and touch your closed fists to the wall. Bend forward slowly; do not bounce. Note: this is a test, not an exercise.

Fitness Aspect: Flexibility

Pass: Yes____ / No_____

Push-up: Lie face down on the floor. Place the hands under the shoulders. Keeping the legs and body straight, press off the floor until the arms are fully extended. Women repeat once, men repeat three times.

Fitness Aspect: Strength

Pass: Yes____ / No_____

Side leg raise: Lie on the floor on your side. Lift your leg up and to the side of the body until your feet are 60 to 90 centimetres (24 to 36 inches) apart. Keep the knee and pelvis facing forward. Do not rotate so that the knees face the ceiling. Perform ten with each leg.

Fitness Aspect: Muscular endurance and strength

Pass: Yes_____ / No____

Getting Physically Fit

How do we know that the physical activity we are doing is really benefitting our physical fitness?

The first thing is to understand what training our bodies is all about. This comes down to Principles of Training. There are three Principles of Training. In other words, in order to train your body you must do three key things:

(a) Specificity:

You must train your heart, lungs and specific muscles in order to improve them.

(b) Use it or lose it:

If you are fit but stop exercising, your fitness level will drop.

(c) Overload:

Your heart, lungs and specific muscles must be stressed beyond their normal level of activity if you are to improve your fitness. You overload through **FITT** [your level of overload MUST be guided by a PE teacher or coach].

FITT is a really simple formula which describes the physical activity you are doing and indicates whether it is really impacting on your physical fitness.

FITT

F = Frequency (How often should I exercise?)
I = Intensity (How hard should I exercise?)
T = Time (How long should I exercise for?)
T = Type (What type of activity?)

In 2010, the World Health Organisation (WHO) used FITT to describe how much physical activity a person should do in order to be physically fit. They recommend that children and young people aged 5–17 years old should accumulate at least 60 minutes of moderate- to vigorous-intensity physical activity daily from a variety of activities.

> If you find it difficult to work out intensity, see the tips on the next page. For types, you can look at pages 180 to 182.

WRITTEN ACTIVITY

1. FITT

(a) Write out FITT for 5- to 17-year-olds according to the WHO guidelines.

Frequency: _____

Intensity: _____

Time: _____

(b) What types of activity do you think would be appropriate for a

(i) 5-year-old

Types: _____

(ii) 17-year-old:

Types: _____

You can also use a fitness tracker to measure your heart rate.

Measuring Intensity of Physical Activity, i.e. how hard should I exercise?

There are two ways in which you can measure the intensity of physical activity:

(a) Using heart rate

(b) Using rate of perceived exertion (RPE): How hard do you think your body is working? In other words, listen to your body.

(a) Using heart rate to measure intensity

Step One:

You can measure your heart rate by measuring your pulse rate.

Using your forefinger and your middle finger, locate your pulse. Count your pulse rate for six seconds and multiply your answer by ten. This gives you your pulse rate for one minute or sixty seconds, i.e. how many times your heart beats in one minute.

Step Two:

To best develop cardiovascular endurance (a fit heart and lungs), there is a range in which the heart needs to work. This is known as the Target Training Zone (TTZ). This term might be familiar to you from Junior Cycle Science and Junior Cycle PE.

Cardio-vascular = heart and lungs

Cardiovascular Endurance is the ability of the heart to provide oxygen to muscles during physical activity for a prolonged period of time

220 is the number of heartbeats in a newborn baby. Every year this number decreases by one. This is why when you calculate your maximum heart rate, you subtract your age from 220.

The Karvonen Formula:

Example: Jenny is 16 years old.

To find her maximum heart rate (HR max), subtract her age from 220.	To find the lower end of her range, multiply HR max by 0.6 (60%).	To find the upper end of her range, multiply HR max by 0.85 (85%).
220 – 16 = 204	204 x 0.6 = 122	204 x 0.85 = 173

Jenny's Target Training Zone is between 122 and 173 heartbeats per minute.

This means for Jenny to get the best value from exercise, she needs to check that her heart rate is always between 122 and 173 beats per minute during exercise. If Jenny's pulse is above her TTZ, she is putting too much pressure on her heart. If her pulse is below her TTZ, she is not working hard enough to get benefit. Your pulse must stay within the TTZ to get the most benefit from exercise.

WRITTEN ACTIVITY

4 2 3
9 5 8
7 1

2. Now find your own Target Training Zone (TTZ)

(a) To find your maximum heart rate (HR max), subtract your age from 220. _____

(b) To find the lower end of your range, multiply HR max by 0.6 (60%). _____

(c) To find the upper end of your range, multiply HR max by 0.85 (85%). _____

(d) Your Target Training Zone (TTZ) is: _____

Once you know your TTZ, you can use this information when you exercise to make sure that your heart rate is within your TTZ. During or after exercise, check your pulse (heart rate) using the 'six second count', as described on the previous page.

(b) Using Rate of Perceived Exertion to measure intensity

Another method of measuring intensity is to rate the difficulty of the exercise on the Borg Scale of Rate of Perceived Exertion (RPE). You should be working between 16 and 20 on this scale to get maximum benefit from exercise (moderate-vigorous exercise).

RPE Scale	Example of Activity
6	No exertion at all
7 Very, very light physical activity	Sitting, reading, watching tv, relaxed
8	
9 Very light physical activity	Walking slowly at own pace
10	
11 Fairly light physical activity	Waking more briskly at own pace
12	
13 Fairly hard physical activity	jogging, tired but still able to continue
14	
15 Hard physical activity	Running hard, healthy person, tired but still able to go on
16	
17 Very hard physical activity	Runnning very hard, healthy person, must push self but still able to go on
18	
19 Very, very hard physical activity	Trying to run fast up a steep hill
20	

Practice using the RPE scale when exercising by estimating your RPE on the scale first and checking it against your heart rate using the six second count.

Take your pulse for six seconds and multiply this figure by ten. This is how many times your heart beats per minute (bpm).

Calculate your results below.

	Warm Up	Aerobic Activity	Cool Down
Rate of perceived exertion			
Heart rate			

When using FITT, the other part which may be difficult to work out is the **Type of Activity.** The information in the next section outlines the types of activity recommended for children, adolescents and adults.

> **Aerobic activity** is physical activity that requires the heart and lungs to work harder to supply muscles and the entire body with oxygen.
>
> An **adolescent** is a person who is going through puberty.

3. Types of Physical Activity Recommended for Children, Adolescents and Adults

In 2010, the WHO outlined physical activity guidelines by life stage.

5- to 17-year-olds

For children and young people of this age group, physical activity includes play, games, sports, transportation, recreation, physical education or planned exercise, in the context of family, school and community activities. To improve cardiorespiratory and muscular fitness, bone health, cardiovascular and metabolic health and reduced symptoms of anxiety and depression, the following are recommended:

1. An accumulation of at least 60 minutes of moderate- to vigorous-intensity physical activity daily.
2. Physical activity of amounts greater than 60 minutes daily will provide additional health benefits.
3. Most of daily physical activity should be aerobic. Vigorous-intensity activities should be incorporated, including those that strengthen muscle and bone, at least 3 times per week.

Moderate-intensity aerobic activities for children and adolescents include:

- Skateboarding
- Cycling
- Brisk walking

Vigorous-intensity aerobic activities for children and adolescents include:

- Cycling
- Skipping

- Running
- Sports such as soccer, basketball and hockey

Muscle-strengthening activities for children and adolescents should include:
- Rope climbing
- Sit-ups
- Tug-of war
- Pull-ups
- Swinging on bars

Bone-strengthening activities for children and adolescents should include:
- Running
- Skipping

18- to 64-year-olds

For adults of this age group, physical activity includes recreational or leisure-time physical activity, transportation (e.g. walking or cycling), occupational (i.e. work), household chores, play, games, sports or planned exercise, in the context of daily, family and community activities. To improve cardiorespiratory and muscular fitness, bone health and reduce the risk of non-communicable diseases and depression the following are recommended:

1. At least 150 minutes of moderate-intensity aerobic physical activity throughout the week, or at least 75 minutes of vigorous-intensity aerobic physical activity throughout the week, or an equivalent combination of moderate- and vigorous-intensity activity.
2. Aerobic activity should be performed in bouts of at least 10 minutes' duration.
3. For additional health benefits, adults should increase their moderate-intensity aerobic physical activity to 300 minutes per week, or engage in 150 minutes of vigorous-intensity aerobic physical activity per week, or an equivalent combination of moderate- and vigorous-intensity activity.
4. Muscle-strengthening activities should be done involving major muscle groups on 2 or more days a week.

Moderate-intensity aerobic activities for adults include:
- Walking briskly (6 kilometres an hour)
- Water aerobics
- Ballroom dancing
- Cycling (16 kilometres an hour)
- General gardening

Vigorous-intensity aerobic activities for adults include:
- Race-walking (6 kilometres an hour)
  (Note: Race-walking is a long-distance athletic event. Although it is a foot race, it is different from running in that one foot must appear to be in contact with the ground at all times.)
- Jogging or running
- Swimming laps
- Skipping

181

✐ Cycling (16 kilometres an hour)
✐ Hiking uphill or with a heavy backpack

Adults should incorporate muscle-strengthening activities at least two days a week. Strength-training activities include:
✐ Weight training
✐ Push-ups
✐ Sit-ups
✐ Carrying heavy loads
✐ Heavy gardening

65-year-olds and above

For adults of this age group, physical activity includes recreational or leisure-time physical activity, transportation (e.g. walking or cycling), occupational (if the person is still engaged in work), household chores, play, games, sports or planned exercise, in the context of daily, family and community activities. To improve cardiorespiratory and muscular fitness, bone and functional health, and reduce the risk of non-communicable diseases, depression and cognitive decline, the following are recommended:

1. At least 150 minutes of moderate-intensity aerobic physical activity throughout the week, or at least 75 minutes of vigorous-intensity aerobic physical activity throughout the week, or an equivalent combination of moderate- and vigorous-intensity activity.
2. Aerobic activity should be performed in bouts of at least 10 minutes' duration.
3. For additional health benefits, adults aged 65 years and above should increase their moderate-intensity aerobic physical activity to 300 minutes per week, or engage in 150 minutes of vigorous intensity aerobic physical activity per week, or an equivalent combination of moderate- and vigorous-intensity activity.
4. Adults of this age group with poor mobility should perform physical activity to enhance balance and prevent falls on 3 or more days per week.
5. Muscle-strengthening activities should be done involving major muscle groups on 2 or more days a week.
6. When adults of this age group cannot do the recommended amounts of physical activity due to health conditions, they should be as physically active as their abilities and conditions allow.

> **RESEARCH**
>
> 1. In what activities do you think this older age group might engage?

4. How Active Am I?

1. Keep a physical-activity diary for a week.

	Example	Monday	Tuesday	Wednesday	Thursday	Friday	Saturday	Sunday
Activity	PE class, rugby, GAA training, Dance, Hockey, Swimming							
Time	2 hours							
Target Training Zone	120bpm and 160bpm							
Skill-related components	Agility, Balance, Coordination, Power, Reaction Time, Speed							
Health-related components	Muscular endurance, Reaction Time, Flexibility, Cardiovascular endurance, Muscular Strength							
Did I meet daily recommendations	YES							

Please make sure to check with your PE teacher to see if your physical activity plan is appropriate. Do not rely on YouTube or websites for physical-activity tips.

What Influences My Physical Activity (PA)

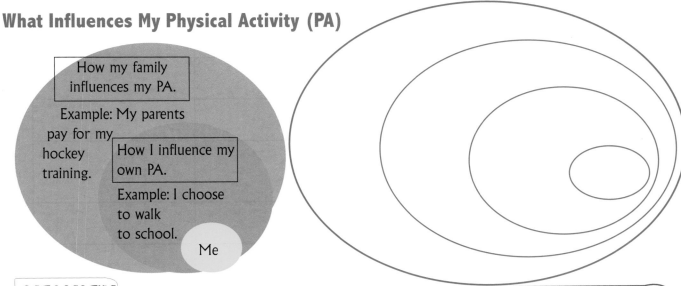

How my family influences my PA.

Example: My parents pay for my hockey training.

How I influence my own PA.

Example: I choose to walk to school.

Me

2. Complete each sphere.

Circle One: How I influence my own PA. Circle Two: How my family influences my PA

Circle Three: How my friends influence my PA. Circle Four: How the wider community influences my PA

TABLE ACTIVITY

3. List all the things that stop you being active and try to find a solution for each.

What stops you from being physically active?	Solutions
Money	Pick an activity that is inexpensive, e.g. jogging, playing football in the park.

RESEARCH

4. Survey of local amenities

Find out what amenities are available for physical activity in your local community and fill in the details in the table below.

Amenity:			
Activities available:			
Cost:			
Phone:			
Email:			
Website:			
Address:			

Look up '50 things to do before you're 11$^3/_4$' at www.nationaltrust.org.uk

S. Body Image

> Body image is the way a person thinks about his or her body and how it looks to others.

Having dealt with physical activity and physical fitness, this section explores the concept of body image and how that impacts on our physical health.

How much do you like your body?

Whether we're aware of it or not, we are influenced by messages about our bodies from our friends, family, advertisements, films and other parts of our culture every day. These external messages may not always agree with our internal knowledge, yet sometimes we act on those messages anyway.

REFLECTION

1. **How easily are you influenced by these external messages?** To find out, tick the statements below that you agree with.

I am constantly thinking about my body size, shape and weight, and I am always working to improve it. _____
I would be much happier and my life would be better if I was thinner or more muscular. _____
I commonly skip meals to lose weight. _____
I weigh myself more than once a day. _____
I know how many calories are in almost every food I eat. _____
I exercise mainly to lose weight or to look better. _____
I completely exclude foods from one food group in order to manage my weight. [Food groups include milk and milk products, fruits, vegetables, breads and grains, meat, beans and nuts.] _____
I don't participate in sports and other activities because I'm embarrassed about my body. _____
I like to wear oversized clothes to hide 'flaws' in my body. _____
I believe there are good foods and bad foods. _____
When I see a model in a magazine I want to look like her/him. _____

If you ticked most of these, you may be trying too hard to fit into an unrealistic body type. It is important to realise that how we feel about ourselves and our bodies should come from within ourselves, not from what our friends think or from models in magazines or on television.

Did You Know?

The genes that we inherit from our mother and father determine 70% of our body weight and shape. This means that we can improve the body we were born with, but only to a certain degree. No matter how hard we try, most of us will never be able to look like Ariana Grande or Harry Styles.

Pictures of models in magazines and advertisements are technically altered. This means that a computer changes their picture by making their legs longer, their stomach flatter and their muscles bigger. Most of the pictures you see in magazines have been altered, and in fact it is humanly impossible to achieve these body types!

The Truth behind the Magazine Covers

Georgina Wilkin, 23, a former model who developed an eating disorder because of the pressures of the job, recognises the phenomenon. 'I've had a few times where I've worked for a magazine and the magazine's come out and I hardly even recognise myself. My legs have been skimmed off, my pores have been eliminated, my nose has been straightened.' The result can be humiliating. 'I felt awful — you feel that what you are as a human being isn't good enough.'

(**Source:** Tulip Mazumdar, What Does It Feel Like to Be Airbrushed?', www.bbc.com)

REFLECTION

2. Why do we feel the need to change how we look? Why do we try to emulate photos of models who have been airbrushed?

_____

_____

_____

_____

_____

RESEARCH

3. Factors that influence our body image

Find and bring to class a photo of someone that you think represents what a teenager should look like — it could be a pop star, an actor, a YouTuber, a model: whatever you think. Break into small groups. Each group should select one photo to discuss in relation to the questions below.

Discussion Questions:
1. Does this pre-teen/teen model represent the perfect body?
2. Can a pre-teen or teen fit in if they are not dressed in the popular styles?
3. Is a person who looks different from the media's representation of cool less worthwhile as a person?
4. How does our culture view attractiveness? How does this differ between men and women?
5. What image do the models project?
6. If the image is taken from an ad, what does the ad want you to feel? What does the ad want you to think?
7. Who do you think this ad would appeal to?
8. What does this ad not show?

9. What is the health message in the ad?
10. Why are people willing to risk their health to get a perfect body?
11. Why is the reality that people come in a variety of shapes and sizes ignored when people try to have the ideal body image?

Bigorexia: John's Story

John is 18 years old and I have taught him physical education for 6 years. At 12 years of age he was morbidly overweight, red-faced, sweating and panting as he moved sluggishly through our school and around the PE Hall. He was the subject of many cruel jibes from his mostly fit male classmates. Many of these jibes were stated openly in class or in the changing room. He was always last to leave the changing room. Reasoning with, reprimanding or punishing his peers never changed the situation. At 14, John began to cycle to school, seemingly oblivious to the comments about his appearance on his bike. He told me he was trying to get fit. He lost two stone that year. However, the taunts continued.

I spoke to individual students again and again but they said that 'John was out of control and was too fat; what did he expect?' When John turned 16, he expressed an interest in learning how to lift weights. As part of PE, his class completed a six-week resistance-training programme. John purchased weightlifting equipment to continue his training at home. In his final year of school, each meeting with John had been punctuated with stories of the progress of John's weights programme and diet.

His body shape had completely changed. He became a slim, smiling mesomorph (muscular). He earned more respect from his male classmates. Boys asked him to help improve their muscle definition. In six years, John had changed from Billy Bunter to GI Joe.

(**Source:** Anonymous PE Teacher)

See also Module 3, Gender Studies, page 67

WRITTEN ACTIVITY

4. Having read John's story, answer the following questions.

(a) Why was John's body shape and size at age 12 not acceptable to his classmates?

_____

(b) What body shape and size is acceptable to boys? Who decides this?

_____

_____

(c) Does it have links with masculinity and what it means to be masculine?

_____

(d) Where do boys learn these messages?

_____

_____

(e) There are some 'warning bells' when reading this story. Yes, he seems healthier as he is no longer overweight and looks fitter. But how did he achieve this?

Was it through:
(i) Over-exercising?
(ii) Eating disordered behaviour?
(iii) Anabolic Steroid use?
(iv) Creatine use?

> **Creatine** is an amino acid that is found in muscle tissue — It can be ingested and causes more muscle tissue to be made.
>
> **Anabolic Steroids** mimic testosterone and cause more muscle tissue to be made.

If a boy wants to lose weight and become fitter, it is important to do this slowly and under the guidance of a PE teacher or a coach. Otherwise, he could develop unhealthy habits which could lead to eating disorders, e.g reverse anorexia/muscle dysmorphia [bigorexia]. In the case of reverse anorexia the medical effects, if using steroids, cause mania, hypomania, high blood pressure, weight gain and thinning of the skin and fluid retention.

Body image is not something we are born with; instead, we learn to become aware of our body image. This learning occurs in the family and among peers, but these only reinforce what is learned and expected culturally.

In today's western culture, women, and increasingly men, are seen to be starving themselves, gorging themselves, alternating between starving and gorging, purging and obsessing — all in order to fit into what society and the media portray as the ideal physical appearance.

Here are some guidelines to help you work towards a positive body image:
1. Listen to your body. Eat when you are hungry.
2. Be realistic about the size you are likely to be based on your genetic and environmental history. There are many different body types: ectomorph, endomorph and mesomorph.
   - People with an **ectomorphic** body shape generally have a light build with small joints and lean muscle. Usually ectomorphs have long thin limbs with stringy muscles. Shoulders tend to be thin with little width.
   - People with an **endomorphic** body shape are solid and generally soft. They may gain fat very easily and are usually of a shorter build with thick arms and legs. Muscles are strong, especially the upper legs.
   - People with a **mesomorphic** body shape have large bone structure, large muscles and a naturally athletic physique. They find it quite easy to gain and lose weight and are naturally strong.
3. Exercise regularly in an enjoyable way, regardless of size.
4. Expect normal weekly and monthly changes in weight and shape.
5. Work towards self-acceptance and self-forgiveness — be gentle with yourself.
6. Ask for support and encouragement from friends and family when life is stressful.

7. Decide how you wish to spend your energy: pursuing the 'perfect body image' or enjoying family, friends, school and, most importantly, life.

Source: *Body Love: Learning to Like Our Looks and Ourselves* by Rita Freeman

Think of it as the three A's . . .
A: Attention — Refers to listening for and responding to internal cues (i.e. hunger, feeling too full, fatigue).
A: Appreciation — Refers to appreciating the pleasures your body can provide.
A: Acceptance — Refers to accepting what is, instead of longing for what is not.

Body Image and Self-Esteem

Self-esteem is a personal evaluation of one's worth as a person. It measures how much you respect yourself.

1. Physical self-esteem:
How happy you are with the way you look.

2. Intellectual self-esteem:
How well you feel you can accomplish your goals.

3. Emotional self-esteem:
How much you feel loved.

4. Moral self-esteem:
How you think of yourself as a person, e.g. a good person or a bad person.

Using the four headings above, apply these to how you feel about yourself. It is important to remember that these feelings often change as we move through our lives. Try to be as honest as you can and remember no one else has to read your personal evaluation. You can use a separate sheet of paper on which to write your response.

Importance of Self-Esteem
- How you see yourself affects every part of your life.
- High self-esteem makes for a happier life. It allows you to be your own person and not have others define you.
- Self-esteem, self-confidence and self-respect are all related to each other.
- Self-esteem is also defined as the judgements a person makes about himself or herself and is affected by self-confidence and respect.
- Self-confidence means we believe in our ability to take action and meet our goals.
- Self-respect is the degree to which we believe we deserve to be happy and have rewarding relationships and how willing we are to stand up for our rights and values.

All these factors affect whether or not we will have a healthy body image.

Making Peace With Your Body and Self

To begin to achieve healthy images of our bodies and ourselves, some changes have to be made.

1. When you look in the mirror, make yourself find at least one good point for every negative you see. Become aware of your positives.

2. Decide which of the cultural pressures — glamour, fitness, thinness, media and peer group — prevent you from feeling good about yourself. If reading fashion magazines, some of which promote an unrealistic body image, makes you feel bad about your body, why not stop buying them?

3. Exercise gets high marks when it comes to breeding positive body feelings. It makes us feel better about our appearance, and improves our health and mood.

4. Emphasise your assets. You've got lots. Give yourself credit for positive qualities. If there are some things you want to change, decide on a plan for how to do this — this plan can be short or long term. Remember: self-discovery is a lifelong process.

5. Make friends with the person you see in the mirror. Say 'I like what I see. I like me.' Say it until you believe it.

6. Question advertisements. Instead of saying 'What's wrong with me', say 'What's wrong with this ad?' Write to the company. Set your own standards instead of letting the media set them for you.

7. Avoid dieting and don't use the weighing scales. Taking these actions will help you to develop a healthy relationship with your body and weight.

8. Challenge size bigotry and fight size discrimination whenever you can. Avoid using phrases such as 'fat slob', 'pig out' or 'thunder thighs'.

9. Be an example to others by taking people seriously for what they say, feel and do rather than how they look.

10. Accept the fact that your body is changing. In teen years, your body is a work in progress. Don't let every new inch or curve throw you off the deep end.

11. You know you are successful when you can look in the mirror and instead of asking 'What's wrong with it', you can say 'There's nothing really wrong with me'. And little by little you'll find you can stop disliking your body.

12. Stop worrying about what others think of you. If you want to change your body, do it for yourself and not anyone else.

13. Have like-minded friends.

GROUP ACTIVITY

1. **Review the research activity on page 186.** Having explored the issue of body image further, discuss in small groups what you now think about the messages that the media can give to younger teenagers.

Body Image and the Media

The media plays a big part in how we form our body image.

Surrounded by thin models and TV stars, teenage girls are taught to strive to reach an impossible goal. As a result, many teenage girls intensely dislike their bodies and can tell you down to the tiniest detail what's wrong with it.

Take a look at the ten most popular magazines on the newspaper racks. The women and men on the covers represent about 0.03 percent of the population. The other 99.97% don't have a chance to compete, much less measure up. Don't forget it's a career for these models. Many have had major body makeovers as well as a full-time personal trainer and chef.

Most ads are airbrushed by computer. Body parts can be changed at the click of a button. The images of men and women in ads today do not promote self-esteem or positive self-image as in general these images do not reflect the reality of people's bodies.

LIST ACTIVITY

2. **The message that 'thin is in' is sold thousands of times a day through TV, movies, magazines, billboards, newspapers and songs.** Can you list a number of media sources where being thin is portrayed as the way to be happy?

_____

_____

_____

_____

_____

_____

Some media sources imply that being thin means being more attractive; however, nothing is more attractive than a happy, healthy person. Not eating enough and being underweight in order to look thin doesn't guarantee happiness, which is often what media sources imply. It is very important to be aware of the benefit of a healthy, well-balanced diet, which often isn't portrayed in media sources.

RESEARCH

3. **Investigate the Dove Campaign for Real Beauty which has been running for the last number of years** (www.dove.com). Identify the reasons why you could see it as an example of positive, honest advertising.

_____

_____

_____

_____

Media Manipulation

Advertising conveys the message 'You're not OK but we can help you fix that. Here's what you need to do.' Teenagers and adults believe it and react to it.

RESEARCH

4. Can you find any adverts in magazines, online or on TV where 'we can fix you' is the underlying message? What other messages are these adverts giving to young people?

When you stop and think about the fact that the average height and weight for a model is 5'10" (1 metre 77) and 110 lbs (50 kgs) and the height and weight for the average woman is 5'4" (1 metre 62) and 145 lbs (65kgs), it's easy to see why this creates a tremendous health risk for young people.

Eating Disorders Common to Adolescents

Considering the amount of time teenagers are exposed to the ideal body image as portrayed by the media, an increasing number of young people, both male and female, are suffering from eating disorders such as bulimia, anorexia nervosa and binge eating.

An eating disorder is a serious disruption to a person's eating habits or appetite which may reflect abnormal psychological behaviour.

Anorexia nervosa and bulimia nervosa are both psychological disorders where the person fears becoming fat or obese. Their image of themselves is distorted and unreal.

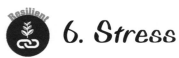

6. Stress

We hear this word very frequently nowadays. But what exactly is it?

Stress is the body's response to any demand made upon it in order to keep the physical body balanced and stable. We term anything that causes stress as being a **stressor**. There are three main categories of stressor.

1. Environmental Stressors
These include heat, noise, overcrowding, climate and terrain.

2. Physiological stressors
These are listed as drugs, caffeine, tobacco, injury, infection, disease or physical effort.

3. Emotional (psychosocial) stressors
In this category, we include any life-changing event, e.g. family illnesses, conflict, deaths of family or friends, increased responsibilities. In school, pressures regarding grades or deadlines for projects or presentations may cause stress.

Interestingly, stress is not always harmful. In fact, too little stress or 'rust out' is not good for health. Moderate stress levels or eustress, as Hans Selye (1978) calls it, are deemed good for healthy growth and maturity. On the other end of the scale, too much stress can result in mental or physical diseases. Such diseases include high blood pressure, heart disease, depression, colitis, ulcers, headaches, insomnia, constipation, diarrohea and back pain. With too much stress we burn out.

RUST OUT ← **Eustress** → **BURN OUT**

Too little stress - Distress   **Too much stress - Distress**

THINK, PAIR, SHARE

1. Talk to your partner and ask the following questions. Write notes on the answers you receive.

(a) Can you describe a stressful situation you have been in?

_____

_____

(b) What type(s) of stressor was involved?

_____

_____

(c) How did your body react?

_____

_____

(d) How did you manage the stressful situation?

_____

_____

Every living creature is in a constant state of some level of stress (some more than others). Some people deliberately put themselves in stressful situations, e.g. sportspeople, surgeons, pregnant women.

LIST ACTIVITY

2. Stressful Jobs

A survey carried out in 2009 by recruitment website www.careercast.com named the 11 most stressful jobs. Can you guess what they were?

_____   _____   _____

_____   _____   _____

_____   _____   _____

_____   _____

The answers are listed upside down at the bottom of the page. How many did you get right? _____

REFLECTION

3. Recognising stress. Answer Yes or No to the following questions.

1.   Do you frequently neglect your diet? _____

2.   Do you frequently try to do everything yourself? _____

3.   Do you frequently snap at people? _____

4.   Do you frequently set unrealistic goals? _____

5.   Do you frequently fail to see the humour in situations others find funny? _____

6.   Do you frequently get easily irritated? _____

7.   Do you frequently make a 'big deal' of everything? _____

8.   Do you frequently complain that you are disorganised? _____

9.   Do you frequently keep everything inside? _____

10.   Do you frequently neglect exercise? _____

11.   Do you frequently have few supportive relationships? _____

12.   Do you frequently get too little rest? _____

13.   Do you frequently get angry when you are kept waiting? _____

14.   Do you frequently ignore stress symptoms? _____

15.   Do you frequently put things off until later? _____

16.   Do you frequently think there is only one right way to do something? _____

17.   Do you frequently fail to build relaxation into every day? _____

18.   Do you frequently spend a lot of time complaining about the past? _____

19.   Do you frequently race through the day? _____

20.   Do you frequently feel unable to cope with all you have to do? _____

Do this exercise alone. If the majority of your answers are 'yes', then you might be feeling stressed. It would be helpful for you to examine ways of 'destressing', e.g. exercise, relaxation, sharing the problem, counselling. Some ways of managing stress are explained in the next section.

miner   air traffic controller   farmer   office manager

inspector   secetary   foreman   laboratory technician   dentist   doctor   labourer

DISCUSS

4. In small groups, discuss how you might recognise that someone was stressed. List five such signs below.

(a) _____

(b) _____

(c) _____

(d) _____

(e) _____

Signs of stress to watch out for:

- gritting teeth
- hunching shoulders
- white knuckles
- biting fingernails
- tapping foot
- sweating
- heart beat faster
- dry mouth
- headache
- back pain

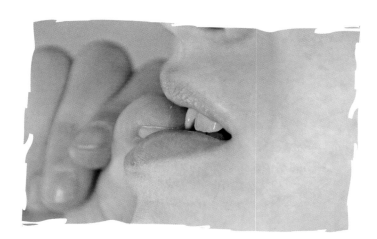

Four Steps to Managing Stress Levels

1. First, identify the situations in your life that make you stressed.

_____

_____

_____

_____

_____

_____

2. Next, use some type of relaxation technique to relieve symptoms of stress. Can you think of any?

_____

_____

_____

_____

_____

_____

3. Third, try to avoid some of the unnecessary stressors in your life.
4. Sometimes we don't have control over situations and we have to accept it and then let it go.

The fitter you are, the better you will be able to cope with stress.

Make sure you have support – home, friends and colleagues.

Balance work with rest and play.

Take action instead of worrying about something.

Prioritise your tasks.

Take exercise.

Take one thing at a time.

Look at stressors as challenges.

If there is no solution, try to accept it by changing your feelings about it.

Don't let little things bother you.

7. Nutrition

Throughout our lives the benefits of a healthy diet and lifestyle will help us to remain healthy and physically fit. Our dietary requirements can change throughout our lives depending on how old we are or if we have a special dietary requirement. Our own awareness about what a healthy diet is and how it can impact on us will influence how important healthy food choices are to us.

Changes in Diet

As we grow and develop from a baby to a toddler to an adolescent and into an adult, our dietary requirements change if we are to remain healthy. Knowing what nutrient requirements are needed at each stage will help you remain fit and healthy and ensure you have a balanced diet.

Consider the food you ate as a three-year-old and the food you eat now as a teenager. Has the quantity of food you eat and the type of food you eat changed?

Adolescents

During the transition from childhood to adulthood, growth spurts are evident. A healthy balanced diet is essential. Gender and physical size will obviously affect the amount and type of food eaten but the following is a general guide as to what you should be eating to remain healthy.

Nutrient	Function	Source
Protein	Growth and hormone production	Meat, fish, eggs, soya products
Fibre	Prevents constipation and bowel disorders	Brown bread, rice, wholemeal pasta
Calcium	Healthy bones and teeth; Prevents osteoporosis	Milk, cheese, tinned fish
Vitamin D	Helps absorption of calcium	Eggs, oily fish
Iron	Prevents anaemia, especially in teenage girls	Meat, dark green leafy vegetables
Vitamin C	Necessary for absorption of iron	Fruit and vegetables
Water	Hydration; healthy skin	Tap/bottled water

- Fatty foods and processed/refined carbohydrate foods should be avoided or kept to a minimum.
- Excesses of these foods could lead to obesity.

The diets of males and females tend to be very similar. However there are some factors that need to be considered:
- Males require a higher daily calorie intake than females.
- Females require a higher quantity of vitamin B12 due to menstruation.
- Males can metabolise (break down) their food faster than females, especially fat-based food.
- Carbohydrate foods, e.g. pasta and potatoes, are important in the diets of young people as they are a good source of energy.
- Females who would like to become pregnant or who are in the early stages of pregnancy (up to 12 weeks) should include folic acid in their diet to prevent the risk of neural tube defects in the foetus.
- All young people need protein in their diet as they continue to grow throughout adolescence.

8. Stress and Nutrition

There are many coping mechanisms we can use when we are stressed. However if we eat the right kind of foods which work in harmony with our body to minimise the effect of a stressful situation, we will feel good about ourselves. Stress management is an excellent tool for helping us with our everyday life. Many foods that you possibly eat already are actually helping you fight stress. We want these foods to release the chemical serotonin, regulate cortisol (magnesium) and improve our immune system.

Food	Effect
Complex carbohydrates, e.g. wholegrain bread, pasta	Slow energy release
Vitamin C, e.g. kiwi fruit, oranges	Helps strengthen the immune system and reduce levels of stress hormone.
Spinach	High in magnesium which helps regulate cortisol levels (stress hormone.
Oily fish	Contains omega-3 fish oils which help protect against heart disease.
Raw vegetables	Mechanical action of chewing crunchy raw vegtables helps release jaw tension.

Final Nutritional Tips
- Limit your salt intake
- Limit caffeine and alcohol intake
- Avoid refined processed carbohydates, e.g. sugary fizzy drinks etc.
- Drink more water

Useful Websites
www.vhi.ie   www.webmd.com/diet

Nutrition
Our food should be our medicine and our medicine should be our food.

Hippocrates (460-377 BC) Greek physician, founder of medicine, who was regarded as the greatest physician of his time

Physical Health
Physical fitness is not only one of the most important keys to a healthy body, it is the basis of dynamic and creative intellectual activity.
John F Kennedy, 35th American President

9. Food during Pregnancy

As with all pregnancies, if a teenage girl is pregnant, a healthy well-balanced diet is essential to help new cells and tissues develop properly in the foetus and mother and to reduce the risk of miscarriage, still birth or other abnormalities at birth.

Link Up
See Module 5: Relationships and Sexuality Education.

Foods to Avoid
- Salt should be avoided as it can cause high blood pressure or oedema, which is water retention.
- Alcohol can cause Foetal Alcohol Syndrome (FAS), which is when a pregnant woman drinks excessively throughout the pregnancy, possibly resulting in the newborn baby being addicted to alcohol, having a low birth weight and other complications.
- Smoking causes a reduction in the body weight of the baby along with other potential problems for the baby (e.g. higher risk of developing asthma and/or other lung problems).
- Raw eggs, unpasteurised cheese or pâté could be a source of food poisoning, e.g. salmonella, listeria. This could increase the risk of miscarriage.

If breastfeeding, follow the nutrient guidelines below but increase your fluid intake.

Nutrient	Function	Source
Folate/folic acid	Reduces neural tube defects, e.g. spina bifida; Folate/folic acid to be taken 12 weeks before conception and for the first 12 weeks of pregnancy	Fortified cereals, supplements, oranges, eggs, wheatgerm
Protein	Synthesis and production of new cells and essential for red blood cells; prevents anencephaly, a neurological disorder which results in a large part of the brain of the developing foetus being absent.	Meat, fish, eggs, soya products
Calcium	Healthy bones and teeth	Milk, yoghurt, cheese
Vitamin D	Increases absorption of calcium by up to 40%	Sunlight, eggs
Iron	Healthy blood in mother and baby; prevents anaemia	Meat, dark green leafy vegetables
Vitamin C	Helps absorption of iron	Fruit and vegetables
Fibre	Prevents constipation, which can be common during pregnancy	Wholemeal and brown products such as rice, pasta, bread
Fatty Acids	Development of nervous system	Oily fish, liver, eggs

10. Essential Food Facts

Daily Energy Requirements	Male Kcal	Female Kcal
Children	1,500	1,400
Adolescents	2,800	2,300
Adult (sedentary)	2,400	2,150
Adult (active)	2,800	2,550
Pregnant		2,400
Lactating (breastfeeding)		2,800
Elderly	2,200	1,800

In September 2016, 'A Healthy Weight for Ireland: Obesity Policy and Action Plan 2016–2025' was launched. The policy and action plan aims to reverse obesity trends, to prevent health complications and reduce the overall burden for individuals, families, the health system and the wider society and economy.

In recent years, levels of overweight and obesity have increased dramatically, with 60% of adults and one in four children in Ireland being either overweight or obese. The cost of adult obesity to society in Ireland is estimated at over €1 billion per annum. Many obesity-related diseases, such as type 2 diabetes, heart disease, liver disease, many types of cancer, sleep apnoea and subfertility, will improve if sufferers can lose and sustain a 10% reduction in their body weight.

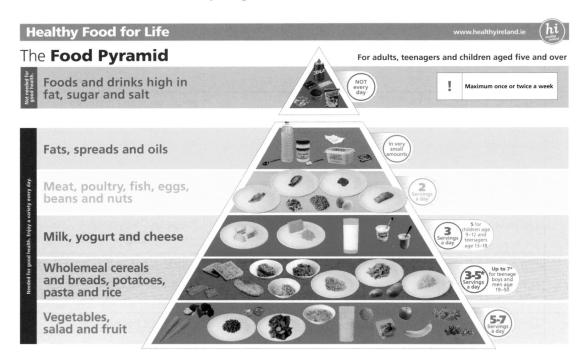

Balanced Eating

By following the Food Pyramid guidelines a variety of foods are eaten in the correct proportion for the nutritional needs of the general population.

Approximately one-sixth of our diet should come from protein sources, one-sixth from fat and two-thirds from carbohydrates including fibre.

Current Healthy Eating Guidelines

- Eat a wide variety of foods following the recommendations of the Food Pyramid.
- Increase your intake of fruit and vegetables to at least five portions a day.
- Replace saturated fats with polyunsaturated alternatives.
- Increase fibre intake.
- Reduce the amount of sugar in your diet.
- Reduce the salt intake in your diet.
- Water intake should be at least eight glasses a day.
- Alcohol, if consumed, should be kept within the recommended guidelines.
- Eat the correct quantity of food for your body size.

Why Do We Eat What We Eat?

The following list shows the main influences on the nutritional choices of teenagers.

A number of factors are within our control while others are not. It is important to remember that some factors will influence us more than others. As we grow, our choices often change as a result of our experiences, e.g. travel, religion etc.

1. Family

Obviously your family diet will be the first influence on you as this is what you are used to eating. But as you experience other types of food through friends and travel, your diet may change to incorporate this variety while your family's diet may remain the same.

2. Friends

As a teenager your peer group and friends can have a much greater impact on what you eat compared to when you were younger. Eating fast food, which is generally high in saturated fat and low in vitamins and minerals, can be an option of choice for many teenagers. Likewise if you have friends who are aware of the nutritional value of their food you are more likely to eat and be aware of the importance of a balanced healthy diet.

3. Culture

Culture plays a fundamental role in food choices, as this is often our first experience of food. Certain foods are associated with specific countries, e.g. pasta is associated with Italy and sushi is associated with Japan.

4. Religion

A person's religion can also influence which foods are eaten, e.g. Hindus are often vegetarian, Muslims don't eat pork and their food is prepared in a special way known as Halal, and Orthodox Jews require food to be Kosher (prepared in a special way).

5. Availability and economic considerations

The availability or ease of access to food will impact on what can be purchased regardless of culture or personal preference. The type and variety of food a person buys will also be influenced by how much money they can afford to spend.

6. Personal preference

Everybody has foods they like or dislike. This obviously affects their choice of food. Some personal preferences can be attributed to special dietary needs, e.g. coeliac, or to a conscious decision such as being a vegetarian or vegan.

7. Sensory aspect

The sight, smell and taste of a food will affect a person's desire to eat a food. The aesthetics (presentation and colour) also contribute to this.

8. Nutritional value

Due to increased media attention and promotion regarding what is healthy food, people are more aware of the benefits of a healthy balanced diet and the role of functional foods in our daily diet. Functional foods claim to have health benefits above basic nutritional value, e.g. probiotic drinks.

9. Advertising and marketing

These have an enormous impact on what people eat. The marketing techniques used involve supermarket layout, e.g. supermarkets organise their aisles so that the food essentials (e.g. bread, milk) are at the back of the shop. Products advertised on TV and in magazines are often endorsed by celebrities in an attempt to influence young people in relation to the food they eat.

No one factor can be highlighted as the main cause of food choice as each factor is influenced by one or more other factors.

11. Food Labels

How Food Labels Can Support Informed Nutritional Decisions

- Food labelling provides teenagers with information regarding their food choice and allows them to make an informed decision.
- Food labelling provides information regarding nutritional content, storage and cooking instructions.
- The Food Safety Authority of Ireland (FSAI) is responsible for ensuring that the EU regulations regarding food labelling are adhered to in Ireland. (www.fsai.ie)
- Since 13 December 2016, it is mandatory to have a nutrition declaration on prepacked foods. The nutritional information now required includes:

  1. The energy value
  2. The amounts of fat, saturated fat, carbohydrate, sugars, protein and salt.

The food label can also include further information regarding nutrients such as monounsaturates, polyunsaturates, polyols, starch and fibre, and any of the vitamins or minerals.

Labelling should be:

- Clear, legible and easy to read (not obstructed).
- In the language of the country where it is being sold.
- Truthful, i.e. it cannot claim that any foodstuffs can prevent, treat or cure disease.

Nutritional Labelling

Nutritional labelling provides information regarding the nutrient content of the food per 100g/ml or per portion.

- If particular claims for a product, such as low sugar content, are made, the content of the specific ingredient must be given particular importance.
- Fortified food must be clearly labelled, e.g. Flora Proactive.

Food labelling is divided into two main areas:

(a) labels for non-packaged foods, e.g. fruit and vegetables.

(b) labels for packaged foods.

Non-Packaged Food

The following information should appear on the shelf from where the food is purchased:

- Name
- Origin (country etc.)
- Class and variety, e.g. Class 1, Class 2, etc. (Class refers to the quality of fresh fruit and veg. Extra Class and Class 1 would be the preferred option.)
- Metric price, e.g. price per kilo

This information can also be displayed on the food wrapping.

Packaged Food

Packaged food is food which comes prepacked from the producer. For example, all processed foods are prepacked.

The following information should appear on the label of any packaged food:

- Name of the food
- Net quantity in metric measurements
- List of ingredients in descending order. Any additives have to be included in the ingredients list.
- Date of minimum durability (sell-by-date)
- Country of origin
- Instructions for storage, use and cooking
- Manufacturer's name and address
- For alcoholic beverages with more than 1.2% alcohol by volume, the alcohol content has to be displayed
- Any genetic modification of the food
- Any added flavourings and sweeteners
- The packing of the food in a modified atmosphere

What do I need to know about food labelling?

Examine the nutritional labels for a Grilled Chicken Caesar Salad and a Crispy Chicken Caesar Salad from McDonalds: (GDA = Guideline Daily Amounts)

	Energy (Kcal) Per Portion/ % GDA	Protein (g) Per Portion/ % GDA	Fat (g) Per Portion/ % GDA	Carbohy-drate (g) Per Portion/ % GDA	Salt (g) Per Portion/ % GDA	Saturated Fat (g) Per Portion/ % GDA	Sugars (g) Per Portion/ % GDA	Fibre (g) Per Portion/ % GDA
Grilled Chicken Caesar Salad	190/10	25/33	7/10	6/2	1.1/22	4/18	3/3	3/12
Crispy Chicken Caesar Salad	350/18	31/41	17/25	19/7	1.6/32	5/23	3/3	4/16

REFLECTION

1. Analyse the two labels above and decide which one provides the most nutritional value and whether or not they are suitable foods for a teenager.

_____

_____

_____

_____

_____

_____

For more information on food labelling, go to www.fsai.ie

What is Genetically Modified (GM) Food?

Genetically modified organisms are used to make genetically modified food. The genetically modified organisms have undergone changes to their DNA structure. DNA controls how big fruit and vegetables grow and how fast they ripen. The EU strictly monitors the use and labelling of GM foods or processes.

Food must be clearly labelled as GM food if:

- It is produced from genetically modified soya beans or maize.
- It has been contaminated with more than 1% of GM soya or maize.
- It contains ingredients with additives and flavourings which have been genetically modified.

Use of Recommended Daily Allowance (RDA)

The RDA shows how many nutrients you should eat each day. On food labels the amount of each nutrient contained in the food is shown under the RDA heading. The figures contained in the RDA were decided by the EU and adopted by each country. These requirements refer to a general population of healthy people.

A more detailed analysis of food composition is available by referring to Dietary Reference Values (DRV). DRVs are used as guidelines with regard to the intake of energy and nutrients for a specific group of people, age and gender. DRVs are generally not found on food labels but can be found at www.indi.ie or www. nutrition.org.uk.

Food Additives

Food additives are substances added to food to improve colour, flavour, texture, nutritional value and shelf life.

A food additive must have a useful and acceptable function before it can be added to the food.

E numbers

The letter 'E' prefixes all tested and accepted additives in the EU.

Agencies/organisations concerned with food additive safety include:
- European Scientific Committee for Food (SCF)
- Joint Expert Committee on Food Additives (JECFA)
- Food and Agricultural Organisation (FAO)
- World Health Organisation (WHO)
- Food Safety Authority of Ireland (FSAI)
- Department of Agriculture and Food

Food Literacy and Food Fluency

Food literacy means having strong food-related skills and knowledge. This is the ability to know how to read food labels and to decide whether the food is healthy or not and its provenance (where it came from). Food fluency is the ability to use food-related skills and knowledge from any media source and determine whether this information can be trusted.

Therefore, a food fluent person can take in and analyse information from multiple sources (digital and otherwise) to make a critical judgement on the quality and provenance of food and project its impact on their health. The central aspects of food fluency are the skills of critical thinking and information literacy.

12. Gender and Nutrition

There are differences and similarities between males and females in relation to their diet and nutrition. Various factors can influence male and female diets.

> Men are from Mars and
> Women are from Venus.
> Dr John Gray, American author

Our diets and eating habits are influenced by our culture and society. In the Western world the word diet has many different meanings but it is mainly associated with trying to lose weight. In other cultures it can refer to the amount of food a person has to eat each day, e.g. Third World countries.

Eating food in the Western world is generally a social event. A study in 2006 by Kirsten Harrison in the University of Illinois in America found that women will eat less food and smaller portions when in the company of men compared to when in the company of women. Both men and women are exposed to an 'ideal' body image via different media sources. This can influence how they view themselves and hence how they interact in a social eating situation.

In trying to be sufficiently masculine, men can over-exercise their upper body and use protein supplements to build muscles, which can have negative health implications if not supervised properly. In contrast, women can diet excessively and over-exercise in an effort to obtain their ideal body weight, becoming underweight for their age and height in the process. These responses come from external cues to the body about what to eat rather than internal cues from when they feel hungry. Thus a man may eat more to appear masculine whereas a woman might eat less to appear feminine.

If a young man uses supplements or steroids and spends excessive time on bodybuilding to create the type of physique he thinks is important, or a young woman focuses too much on calorie intake and energy expenditure during exercise, they could cause great damage to their bodies.

DISCUSS

1. As a class, debate the following statement:
Teenagers abuse their bodies by choosing foods that make 'body beautiful' promises over nutritional value.

RESEARCH

2. Gender differences and diet
   (a) Examine the differences and similarities between male and female eating habits and their behaviour and attitudes in relation to diet and nutrition.
   (b) Identify the different pressures exerted on males and females in relation to diet.

REFLECTION

3. Fill in the table below to show if you have a good balance between your physical activity needs and your nutritional needs.

| | Exercise | | Resting | | Eating | | |
Day	Activity	Time Spent	Rest	Sleep	Breakfast	Lunch	Dinner
Example	Walked to school	20 mins	1 hr TV	6 hours	Cereal, toast, juice	Sandwich, apple, Coke	Fish, Mash, Peas
Monday							
Tuesday							
Wednesday							
Thursday							
Friday							
Saturday							
Sunday							

13. Your Life Plan: How Has It Changed?

PERSONALITY TYPE

1. Circle your personality type below. You identified this already in the Life Plan at the beginning of the book.

2. Your personality can directly impact how you understand, accept or reject some of the concepts in this module. What changes or challenges are ahead of you?

    _____

    _____

    _____

3. How might you learn to deal with these changes or challenges? Think of your multiple intelligences. These may offer clues as to how you may best approach these changes or challenges.

    _____

    _____

    _____

REALITY CHECK

4. Thinking about what we've explored in this module, fill out your Wheel of Life again.

(a) Has anything changed?   Y ☐   N ☐

(b) If so, what has changed and why?

    _____

    _____

(c) Do you need to take action in any area? Y ☐   N ☐

(d) If so, what actions do you need to take?

    _____

    _____

    _____

(e) Identify who might help you achieve these actions.

    _____

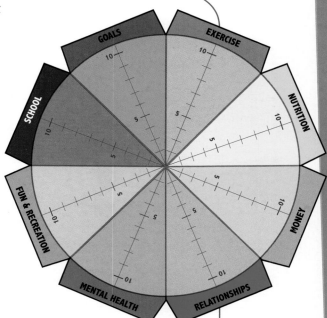

GOALS

5. Do you need to set a goal for this area in your life? If so, go to page 223 for a Goal Worksheet.

Module 7:
Self-Management (Part 2)

Introduction

In this section we will be looking at some of the options and choices you may have to make in the coming year regarding what you will be doing once you leave post-primary school. It can often be a daunting task as you may be unsure of what choices to make with respect to college, work, where to live, budgeting etc. Remember the decision-making process you have used throughout the last number of years and adapt and use it for these decisions about your life after school.

And remember sometimes we make good choices and other times we make not-so-good choices but that's ok. We can learn from every experience we have.

As you are currently studying to do your Leaving Certificate exam, you might have already decided which subjects you will sit. When you made these decisions at the beginning of Fifth Year, you may or may not have known what you would like to do once you leave school.

It is still possible that you are unsure about what you would like to do once you have finished school. Exploring the options available to you is a good place to start and hopefully the following sections will guide you.

1. Options

Each student is an individual. You have your own motivational factors and ambitions regarding what you would now like to achieve in life.

The following are some of the options you might choose:

- Study at a third level college
- Do an apprenticeship
- Repeat your Leaving Cert exam
- Go into the workforce .
- Go travelling
- Do voluntary work
- Other: _____

> The best decisions are usually made when you are well informed about the options and it feels right.

The list could go on but the options listed on the previous page are some of the most popular options for young people in Ireland today.

In order to decide what you want to do you probably need to carry out some form of assessment on what you like doing, what you are interested in, what skills you have etc.

The five areas I am most interested in are:

1. _____

2. _____

3. _____

4. _____

5. _____

Decision-Making Steps

If you remember back to your Junior Cycle SPHE classes, you spent some time on the decision-making process.

Use the following questions to help you gain a greater insight into one of the options you have chosen above.

WRITTEN ACTIVITY

1. Decision Making

(a) What are the pros and cons of the choice/option?

_____

_____

(b) How will this option fit with my skills, personality, values and interests?

_____

_____

(c) Have I spoken to other people whose opinions I value about the option?

_____

_____

(d) If I pick this option how will I feel — happy, excited, sad, relieved etc.?

_____

_____

(e) What or who is the most motivational/influential aspect of this option? In other words, am I considering this option because of friends, family or finance?

_____

_____

(f) Having answered the above questions, how do you feel about the option/options now?

_____

_____

2. Force Field Analysis

(a) In the template below, write your chosen option. In the arrows on the left-hand side, identify and list the pros of your option. On the right-hand side, identify and list the cons.

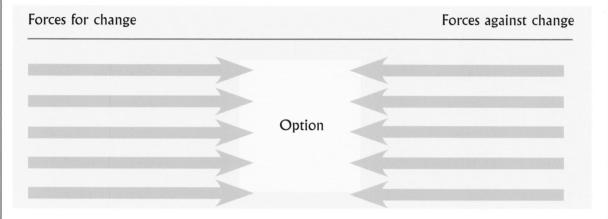

Forces for change   Forces against change

Option

(b) Study your lists of pros and cons and decide whether you should choose the option or not.

2. Career Action Plan

You will do a more detailed career action plan in your guidance class so this section is simply a revision exercise for you – or it could be your preparation for when you do the plan in greater detail.

Goal Setting

You have set goals throughout your life so far. In SPHE class at Junior Cycle you may have had a long-term goal of completing your Leaving Cert exam and now you are nearly there.

When setting goals you should consider the SMARTER principle:

- **S**pecific (exact, precise and detailed)
- **M**easurable (it can be measured, quantifiable)
- **A**chievable (realistic, possible)
- **R**elevant (related, appropriate)
- **T**imed (timescale)
- **E**valuated (weigh up and assess)
- **R**eviewed (go over, reconsider, look at)
  Source: www.careersportal.ie

WRITTEN ACTIVITY

1. SMARTER

(a) Why do you think it is important to apply the SMARTER principle to your goals?

_____

_____

_____

(b) Why is it important to you to achieve your goals?

_____

_____

_____

(c) Outline the benefits of achieving your goals.

_____

_____

_____

Setting goals is the first step to turning the invisible into the visible. Tony Robbins, lifecoach.

GROW

The **GROW** model is often used in coaching:

> **G** – What is your **goal**?
> **R** – What is the **reality** of the situation?
> **O** – What are the **options** available?
> **W** – What is the plan / **way forward**?

TABLE ACTIVITY

2. Following the GROW model, fill in the table below for a goal you would like to achieve.

Goal	
Reality	
Options	
Way Forward	

Note: You may not always achieve your goals in the timeframe you have given yourself so be realistic with your expectations of when you will get there.

What Skills Do I Have?

Skills can be divided into three main categories.

1. **Transferable:** These skills can be used in a variety of settings, e.g. the skill of being able to persuade or influence people.
2. **Specialist:** These are more specific skills and are gained through work experience or training in a particular area.
3. **Self-Management:** These skills can be used in a variety of settings and refer to how you manage yourself at work, e.g. timekeeping.

TABLE ACTIVITY

3. Use the table below to **(a)** list your skills, **(b)** identify which type of skill each is, and **(c)** assess whether your skills could be improved.

Skill	Type	Level

Suiting Your Career to Your Skills

Now that you have looked at your skills base, complete the following worksheet to help you decide which job/career path might suit you best.

Job Research Table

The job I would like to do is _____

Job Basics

1. What would I be doing in this job? _____

_____

2. What skills do I need for this job? _____

_____

3. What qualifications do I need? _____

_____

4. How competitive is it to gain entry to this job? _____

_____

5. What will help me gain entry? _____

_____

Work Environment

1. Where in the world will I be working? _____

_____

2. Who will I be working with (e.g. a sales team, on your own)? _____

_____

3. Where will I live? _____

_____

Financial Implications of the Job

1. How much will I earn? _____

_____

2. Will I receive bonuses? _____

_____

3. Will I be able to study and still get paid? _____

_____

4. Are there any other benefits to the job, e.g. health insurance? _____

_____

Future

What are the future prospects of the job? _____

_____

Life Balance

1. How does this job fit in with the rest of my life? _____

_____

2. Does this job suit me as a person, the qualities and values I have? _____

_____

3. Does this job interest me? _____

_____

4. How would I feel if I didn't get this job/career option? _____

_____

Look back over your answers to the questions and discuss with your parents/guidance counsellor/ friends whether or not this job is suitable for you.

How Would I Like to Work?

Now that you have an idea of the type of career that might suit you, let's see what type of working conditions are important to you.

(**Note:** This activity might help you make your final decision regarding the best career for you.)

In each of the seven categories below, choose the working condition that most appeals to you.

1. I would like my work hours to be:
- 9 to 5 / 5 days a week ☐
- flexible hours ☐
- self-employed ☐
- part-time ☐
- shift-work ☐

2. I would like to work:
- alone ☐
- with other people ☐
- with people of my sex only ☐
- with older people ☐
- with younger people ☐
- with people of a similar age to me ☐
- with people from other cultures ☐
- with people from my own culture ☐
- with people I mix with socially ☐
- other ☐

3. The working conditions I would most value are:
- working outdoors ☐
- working indoors ☐
- working in an office ☐
- working quietly ☐
- working surrounded by activity ☐
- answering to a boss ☐
- having my autonomy/working independently ☐
- having my own office ☐
- other ☐

4. Security of my job is:
- very important to me ☐
- I prefer working in a well-established role ☐
- I prefer working for a newly-created company ☐

5. What type of leadership would I like?
- I prefer to be led ☐
- I want to lead others ☐
- I need to admire and respect my boss ☐
- I want to help others ☐

- I don't need feedback ☐
- I need plenty of feedback ☐
- I want rewards for jobs that I do well ☐
- I need to feel my boss is approachable ☐

6. What are the rewards and financial aspects of the job I would like?
- A good starting salary ☐
- Good future prospects / Training prospects ☐
- Working for commission ☐
- Receiving performance bonuses ☐
- Receiving overtime pay ☐
- Receiving plenty of holidays ☐
- Doing lots of travel ☐
- Receiving fringe benefits (e.g. company car) ☐
- Receiving staff discounts ☐

7. What work challenges do I feel I need?
- I prefer routine work ☐
- I like working to deadlines ☐
- I want plenty of variety ☐
- I need lots of challenges ☐
- I seek the chance to be creative and innovative ☐
- I'm prepared to start at the bottom level of
  the company / workplace ☐
- Other ☐

8. Select the most important point for you from each of the previous seven categories. List these seven points below.

(a) _____

(b) _____

(c) _____

(d) _____

(e) _____

(f) _____

(g) _____

CV

If you're applying for a job, whether it's part-time or the first step in your career, you'll need a Curriculum Vitae, or CV. Different types of CVs can be used but the most common one is the chronological one, where each section is ordered according to when the relevant items were achieved.

Your CV will often focus on your education, qualifications, hobbies / interests and work experience, although this work experience may not be directly related to the course or job you are now applying for. You can also add a brief 'About Me' section, where you can describe yourself and your positive qualities in a few sentences.

You will also need some referees — these are people who can vouch for your character. They could be former employers or someone in a position of responsibility, such as a school principal. Always ask permission from your referees to list them. If you have written references from your referees, you can attach them to your CV, but often nowadays an employer will email or phone your referee instead. When you're applying for a job, it's a good idea to let your referees know that they may be contacted so they are prepared.

CURRICULUM VITAE OF _____

Personal Details

Name: _____

Address: _____

Date of Birth: _____

Mobile Number: _____

Email: _____

Education

Primary school: _____

Dates attended: e.g. 2005–2012 _____

Secondary school: _____

Dates attended: _____

Examinations Taken

Junior Certificate: Year of examination

Subject	Level	Grade
E.g. English	Higher or Lower	e.g. A
_____	_____	_____
_____	_____	_____
_____	_____	_____
_____	_____	_____
_____	_____	_____
_____	_____	_____
_____	_____	_____
_____	_____	_____
_____	_____	_____

Leaving Certificate: Year of examination

Subject	Level	Grade
_____	_____	_____
_____	_____	_____
_____	_____	_____
_____	_____	_____
_____	_____	_____
_____	_____	_____
_____	_____	_____

Transition Year: _____

Work Experience

Start with your most recent experience

Job title: e.g Shop assistant
Date: e.g. 2 June–4 August 2018
Employer: e.g. Better Books
Duties: e.g. Serving customers
                     Using the till
                     Organising stock
                     Pricing stock

Job title: e.g. Work experience student
Date: e.g. 1–5 March 2018
Employer: _____
Duties: _____

Interests and Hobbies

List any sports you play or activities you enjoy – e.g. tennis, reading, cooking, guitar, hurling

Achievements

Things you have achieved, in or out of school – e.g. member of student council, member of winning debating team, battle of the bands winner

About me

Optional short piece about your positive qualities and what they could bring to an employer.

Referees

Supply **two** – this can be someone you've worked for or someone who can vouch for your character (principal, coach etc.)

Name: _____   **Name:** _____

Position: What their job title is   **Position:** What their job title is

Address: _____   **Address:** _____

Phone: _____   **Phone:** _____

Email: _____   **Email:** _____

3. College Applications

If you decide to attend college/university, there are a number of options available to you. Your guidance counsellor will have all the details you need regarding what to do, how to fill out the forms and when the closing dates fall etc.

The following websites might be useful to you as well:

www.cao.ie	College applications in Ireland
www.ucas.co.uk	College applications in the UK
www.qualifax.ie	A comprehensive guide to Third Level education
www.careersportal.ie	Links to other websites which will help you decide what is best suited to you.
www.ncge.ie	Guidance counselling in Ireland

Get Organised

As you gather the career information you need, have a folder where you keep all this detail. Use dividers to separate the information on each college/work placement etc. and write important dates in your diary. The more people you talk to about your chosen career or job option, the greater the understanding you will have about the work involved after you have your qualifications.

> Use your mobile phone to put in any reminders for closing dates, interviews etc. This way you won't miss any deadlines.

4. Budgeting and Accommodation

Budgeting

Budgeting is a plan for spending and it ensures your expenditure and your income are balanced. If you are spending more than you earn, you will get into debt very quickly.

You might decide to have a weekly or a monthly budget depending on when you pay your rent or receive an income. However in college, or when you start work, it is advisable to have a weekly budget at first. Avoid using credit cards, as these bills can build up very easily. Some banks offer to insert a small sum into new credit card accounts; however, you should seriously consider whether a credit card is the right payment method for you. Bad management of a credit card can lead to significant stress and financial worries. It can also affect your credit rating long after you have finished college.

It is also a good idea to use a pay-as-you-go mobile phone rather than a billed mobile phone. That way you will have a very clear idea of how much money you are spending on phone bills.

TABLE ACTIVITY

1. Fill in the table below with your approximate costing of spending during one week in college / working away from home where you would have all of the following expenses:

Income / Wage / Grant / Other	Expenditure	
1.	Rent	
2.	Food	
3.	Electricity	
4.	Heating	
5.	Transport	
6.	Mobile phone	
7.	Books	
8.	Clothes	
9.	Entertainment	
10.	Medical	
TOTAL:	TOTAL:	

If you do get into financial difficulty, contact the Money Advice and Budgeting Service MABS (www.mabs.ie) who will be able to provide you with practical advice and guidance to help your situation. MABS can also help you plan and draw up a suitable budget. They will also provide you with a Financial Resource pack if you contact them.

FAQs

1. What are the advantages of budgeting?
   - Prevents overspending
   - Provides for unexpected expenses
   - Limits the use of credit cards etc.

2. Where / How can I pay my bills?
   - Most bills can be paid at your local post office.
   - A direct debit can be set up so the money comes directly out of your current account when the bill is due.
   - Register at www.billpay.ie and then you can pay most bills online.

Accommodation

If you need to live away from home when working or at college, it is important that you know your rights as a tenant. **Threshold** is Ireland's best guide to tenants' rights so if you encounter any difficulties, contact them immediately and they will be able to advise you **(www.threshold.ie)**. **Citizens Information Centres** around the country will also be able to provide you with advice and contacts on this issue **(www.citizensinformation.ie).**

Where do I start?

- Contact your college which will have a list of possible accommodation options.
- Check out the ads in local evening papers for suitable student accommodation.
- Finally, check www.daft.ie which shows listings of accommodation to rent everywhere in Ireland.
- Always check out the condition of the accommodation before you agree to rent it.

🖊 Check to see if electricity and heating bills are included in the rent or are separate.

🖊 Read the tenancy agreement fully. Even get another person, e.g. a parent, to check it for you.

🖊 Note the condition of appliances etc. in the dwelling and report any faults to the landlord immediately.

Staying Grounded

Whatever decision you make about where to start your next chapter, it is still very important to look after your emotional and mental health, especially through a time of such great change.

Keep investing in your interests, your skills and talents and join as many groups or clubs that are of interest to you. They may appear impressive on your CV further down the line.

Your life goals can guide you in terms of possible careers, but remember to also keep a balance between work and play. Don't forget that plans can change or be refined as you gain more information about yourself and the world.

Talk to friends and family, start networking where possible, stay engaged with the here and now and involve new and old friends along the way.

Helpful Websites

www.spunout.ie
www.yourmentalhealth.ie
www.socialanxietyireland.com

No one knows what he can do til he tries.
Publilius Syrus, Roman author

Well begun is half done.
Aristotle, Greek philosopher

There are no shortcuts to any place worth going.
Beverly Sills, American opera singer

5. Your Life Plan: How Has It Changed?

PERSONALITY TYPE

1. Circle your personality type below. You identified this already in the Life Plan at the beginning of the book.

2. Your personality can directly impact how you understand, accept or reject some of the concepts in this module. What changes or challenges are ahead of you?

_____

_____

_____

3. How might you learn to deal with these changes or challenges? Think of your multiple intelligences. These may offer clues as to how you may best approach these changes or challenges.

_____

_____

_____

REALITY CHECK

4. Thinking about what we've explored in this module, fill out your Wheel of Life again.

(a) Has anything changed?   Y ☐   N ☐

(b) If so, what has changed and why?

_____

_____

_____

(c) Do you need to take action in any area? Y ☐   N ☐

(d) If so, what actions do you need to take?

_____

_____

_____

(e) Identify who might help you achieve these actions.

_____

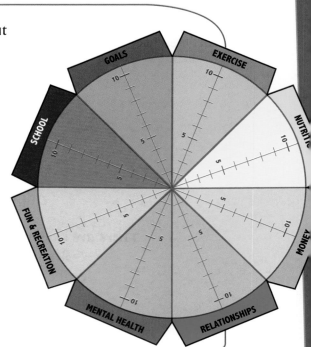

GOALS

5. Do you need to set a goal for this area in your life? If so, go to page 223 for a Goal Worksheet.

Goal Worksheet

Milestone	Brief description of activities needed to achieve this goal	Why is this important?	Resources	Timing
Milestone 1				
Milestone 2				
Milestone 3				
Milestone 4				
Milestone 5				
Milestone 6				
Goal achieved				

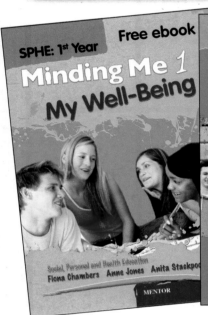
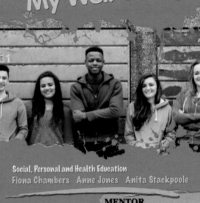